AND THEN MY UTERUS FELL OUT

A memoir on life with pelvic organ prolapse

P.R. Newton

The information and ideas in this book are not intended as a substitute for professional medical advice. Before attempting any new treatments you should consult your personal physician. If medical advice or other expert help is needed, the services of an appropriate medical professional should be sought.

Events and conversations have been recalled to the best of my ability. Names have been changed.

ISBN: 978-0-9920232-4-9

NOTE

In putting together this work of non-fiction, I have recreated conversations and situations to the best of my ability using my journals, memory, and conversations with loved ones. I have chosen to use pseudonyms.

AND THEN MY UTERUS FELL OUT

A memoir on life with pelvic organ prolapse

Table of Contents

DEDICATION

To my boys, all three of them.

Introduction

This book is about something millions of women suffer from but no one wants to talk about: pelvic organ prolapse - commonly known as POP or, simply, prolapse. A condition where a woman's pelvic organs slip out of place, causing all sorts of grief.

During the process of putting this story on paper, I decided to be brutally honest and use words that would make your momma choke on her afternoon tea. I talk about the uterus, cervix, bladder, and - OMG - the rectum! This book also talks about bowel movements, going pee, menstrual cycles and, yup, the down and dirty, sex.

My mother is so proud!

According to the American Urogynecologic Society (AUGS), pelvic organ prolapse affects more than half of all women. In most cases it occurs later in life; but not always. Not in my case. The lifetime risk that a woman will have surgery for the correction of prolapse or urinary incontinence in the United States is about 11%.

Many women will never admit to having issues with bladder control or prolapse. The shame, fear, and lack of knowledge are just too great. Or perhaps they see it as a natural part of aging. But the trend is changing. Women no longer want to go placidly into old age. They want to fight it, keeping their bodies fit and active well past menopause. But when your internal organs start making a sprint for the light, it can make those dreams seem impossible to achieve.

What has happened to my body is absurd in so many ways. This was definitely not in any sex ed classes. I find humor has been a great tool during my healing. Not that I am healed, prolapse is an ongoing condition, but I am in a good place. A place I will share more about later.

A surprising thing happened as I put pen to paper for my story; I discovered that my journey has been about far more than pelvic organ prolapse. It is also about grief, depression and the struggles of motherhood. To share only one facet of my journey would have been like painting only a corner of the canvas. Even if you do not suffer from prolapse, I hope you will find some universal truths in my story that all mothers share.

I have divided my story into five parts. Part one is about my life before I developed prolapse, when I lived in complete ignorance about the frailty of my womanly parts. Part two covers the first year following my son's birth, when my life was irrevocably changed and my future was an unknown entity that filled me with fear. Part three covers a period of three years when I explored surgery and struggled to come to terms with the fact that I was facing a permanent disability as I tried to parent two young boys. Part four talks about how I took control of my life and started living again. Finally, part five talks about what it has been like living with prolapse over the past eight years, what life looks like today, and where I see myself going in the future.

Not comfortable talking about your womanly parts? No worries; I will do all the talking. I'm committed to sharing my story with brutal honesty. So pour yourself a cuppa, or maybe something stiffer (it helps with the humor bit), sit back and relax. Thank you for joining me on this journey.

What is Pelvic Organ Prolapse?

I suspect that most of my readers will be familiar with this condition, but just in case you are new to prolapse, I will provide a brief summary. This book is not a self-help book or guide to pelvic organ prolapse; it is simply my story of living with this condition for eight years. As with any medical condition, if you have concerns about your own body or health consult your doctor or, better yet, find a pelvic floor specialist.

Now back to POP. What is it?

People have written whole books to answer this question, but to keep it in the simplest terms, it is when the pelvic organs - such as the bladder, uterus and rectum - slip down from their proper positions.

Statistics for POP vary, but the most commonly used statistic is that 50% of women will develop pelvic organ prolapse during their lifetime. Many women develop some degree of prolapse following vaginal deliveries. This type is usually temporary and experiences a significant amount of spontaneous healing. The other type of POP is permanent, most commonly occurring in women after menopause. But not always. Not in my case, and not in the case of a surprisingly high number of women I have met over the years.

And yet, with all these women suffering, most people have never heard of pelvic organ prolapse. Why? Well because most women suffer in silence. That is one of the main reasons I decided to share my story. I don't understand why no one is talking and I think it is time to break the silence. The depression, grief and shame associated with this condition are only made worse by a feeling of loneliness. My goal in sharing my story is that women suffering from prolapse will not feel so alone.

I am far from the first to try and break the silence. There are a number of people out there dedicated to making this topic heard. If you need help, please look. Help is out there. I am simply adding my voice in a way I think will be helpful, by sharing my personal story. I am not a medical professional. I am simply a woman learning how to live in a new body I inherited through a series of unfortunate events.

POP is not just a postpartum or old lady condition. It can happen to women at almost any age, from teenagers to seniors. Although the number one cause is vaginal birth, many other things can cause prolapse as well. Pregnancy (with delivery by C-section) can still result in prolapse, especially if the C-section is done after labor has started. Other causes include chronic constipation, weight lifting or lifting heavy weights repeatedly, impact exercises (like running or gymnastics), poor diet, obesity, long lasting cough (from asthma or smoking), trauma or injury, disease or tumors, and connective tissue disorders, just to give a few examples.

There are many ways pelvic organs can prolapse, or fall down towards the vaginal opening. In general, the issue is not actually with the organs but instead with the connective tissues, muscles, tendons and ligaments, stretching or becoming damaged and therefore are unable to hold the organs in place.

Gravity truly is the biggest enemy when dealing with POP.

I assume if you are reading this book it is because you have pelvic organ prolapse, but if you don't and are curious about the symptoms, here are a few of the most common signs of prolapse:

- Loss of bladder or bowel control (including an inability to 'hold it').
- Frequent and/or incomplete urination.
- Difficulty urinating or having bowel movements.
- Pressure, heaviness, and pain in the pelvic area.
- Lower back pain.
- Inability to use a tampon.
- Pain during intercourse.
- Bulging tissues in the vaginal canal, sometimes bulging outside the body.
- Pain (and perhaps sagging or bulging) of the perineum.

Sadly this condition is rarely taken seriously in the medical profession but, as you will see from my story, it has incredibly far reaching ramifications for quality of life.

Thankfully there is a great deal that can be done to help alleviate the symptoms of POP naturally. Things like diet, exercise, supplements, supportive devices, hormone therapy, physical therapy, and living healthy can all provide relief and sometimes long term improvement. Surgery is also an option but one that requires research, and should not be entered into lightly.

The biggest battle most women face is the psychological impact of POP. Having your girly parts broken is devastating for most women. Hop onto any online prolapse support group and you can immediately feel the tensions running high. Too many women are shattered and embarrassed by this condition; so much so that it is estimated that only 30% of women with prolapse symptoms will seek any medical attention.

Women need to be properly educated about POP; the lack of knowledge is astonishing. It affects women all over the world and it doesn't discriminate based on race, wealth, health, or beliefs. Too many women are suffering in silence.

As I share my story please remember this is my personal journey. Yours may, and will, be very different. My story is not meant, in any way, to provide medical advice. What has worked for me may not work for others. I do believe that experimentation is key to helping your body find a healthy balance, whether you have prolapse, or a bad back, or weight issues. Health is balance. There are so many tools and treatments available. You never know what might be the key to your wellness. I believe the most important thing you can invest in is yourself. The return on that investment is priceless.

As I mentioned earlier, I wrote this book to fill what I see as a huge gap: the deafening silence around this condition. I see so many struggling with this condition alone and with a stiff upper lip. By sharing my journey openly and honestly, I hope at least a few people will feel less alone in their struggles.

At the time of publication (Autumn 2013), I am approaching eight years postpartum. Eight years of living with severe prolapse. It can be done. Today I am healthier, stronger and braver than I have ever been. Prolapse, in all of its devilish ways, played a big part in getting me here.

So with that, here is my story.

PART 1

LIFE BEFORE

Me Without the Mother Part

Before I had kids, I was self-assured, confident, ready to take on the world. Aren't all twenty somethings like that? I was successful because I was passionate, and dedicated to being the absolute best I could be, in everything I did. I worked hard, I put in long days (often starting at 8 a.m. and not leaving the office until 11 p.m.), and long work weeks. I climbed the corporate ladder like a greyhound chasing a rabbit. Nothing was going to stop me from catching the big prize.

I showed this passion for everything, not just my career. My mother used to joke that I was the only six year old she knew who had a five year plan; a plan that was updated constantly. It included everything. I drew up blueprints for what my future home would look like, how many animals I would have, and even drafted budgets.

I grew up on the prairies of Canada. My childhood was a happy one, filled with everything a little girl could want, including ponies. Yes, I had ponies! But I was also painfully shy. The consummate geek, with a mane of wild curly hair and over-sized, thick glasses. Oh, and an obsession with Doctor Who and computers, which is still true to this day.

I was never one of the cool kids. I wasn't pretty enough, social enough. At times it bothered me, like when they started hosting school dances, events designed to do nothing but separate the socially awkward even more from the group, but for the most part I was able to brush it off. I preferred the company of my animals to people, anyway.

On the spectrum of childhoods mine was a good one, filled with lots of happy memories and a stable, close family. My only complaint? I never got to travel. All our money and time went into the horses and other animals. I had the travel bug but had to wait until adulthood to feed that desire.

University was one of the greatest times of my life. Not only did I meet the man of my dreams, but I discovered the power of education, of learning about the world. Before university I was a mediocre student at best, with a love-hate, mostly hate, relationship with school. This love of learning arriving so late in my schooling was surprising. I couldn't believe I was enjoying school. I threw myself into my education, and with the exception of chemistry (oh chem how we hated each other!), I really enjoyed my classes and even became a research assistant.

The best part? University embraced the geeky awkwardness that was me. I had finally found a place where I belonged.

My hobbies were time consuming passions. Horseback riding, my obsession from childhood, followed me into adulthood as I grew from ponies to racehorses to warmbloods. I spent, many, many hours in the barn, learning about all aspects of equine husbandry. Early on, I dedicated myself to competing in horse trials. In high school and University, with school taking up more of my time, my focused turned to breeding and training young horses. The demands the young horses made on me were much less than the rigors of competition training.

A love of horses flowed easily into a love of all animals. To this day, I love being surrounded by furry and hairy little creatures. My asthma begs to differ with me on this love, but the heart wants what the heart wants and that is why they invented air filters and hardwood floors.

At eighteen years old, as I was entering my second year of university, I met a man seven years my senior. He had long raven black hair and rode a motorcycle. His name was Remy and within three weeks I knew he was the love of my life. Seven years later I married him, in a beautiful ceremony in a theater, our vows shared from the stage as our family and friends cheered us on.

The stage was a big part of our lives in the early years of our relationship. Remy convinced me to join an acting and role-playing group. Surprisingly, I found it a lot of fun and participated for many years. Somehow I always seemed to land the role of the queen or kick-butt heroine. It felt really good to break out of my shell and embrace these characters. I learned a lot during that time about how to present myself and hide my insecurities; something that helped me in my future career.

So if I seem a little overly dramatic at times, know that I come by it honestly. I love a little drama! But in the vein of truth and honesty, I will tell you my Drama Queen crown is a little tarnished with Play-Doh now.

I know, that was totally the kind of truth you were looking for in this book, wasn't it?

After graduating with a psychology degree I stayed on at the university as a research assistant for two years before finally moving out into the real world, where I landed a job working in public relations and project management with the government. While working I continued to take courses and training in my chosen field, and was quickly promoted into management before I was twenty-five years old.

Life was good. No, that's not strong enough. My life was blessed. My life was amazing. I had the love of my life. I had lots of friends and family, and many hobbies and passions. We traveled a lot, something I had dreamed of doing as a child. Planning and preparing for each trip was so exciting, the perfect focus for my need to organize, research and plan. Getting off the beaten path, and learning about other cultures, was our favorite way to travel.

Even though my life was filled with things I loved, it was stressful. Instead of cutting back to cope with the stress, I added more. I discovered yoga, the ultimate stress relief, I was told, and once again my passion was ignited. I was naturally athletic, despite the whole geek thing; years working in the barn had always kept me very fit. Yoga came easily, naturally, and felt so good as I used it to let the tension and stress go. I trained and practiced until I was ready to start my teacher training certificate.

At twenty-eight years old, things started to change. A shadow started to creep in. At first I ignored it. Even when the doctors warned me, pointing out that my body was starting to fight back, I ignored them. My blood pressure was up, my cholesterol was high, I battled insomnia, and I started having heart palpitation or tachycardia episodes. But I was still in my twenties, I argued with my doctor - and myself - I was invincible. Young. With so much hope and drive to achieve so much. I just needed to push harder and everything would be fine.

It started slowly, sneaking in around the edges where I tried to pretend it didn't exist. But it was there and getting stronger, the embers of a burn out becoming hotter and hotter. The hours, the pressure, the politics, the drama; it became too much. Working sixty hours, often more, every week, the pressure to constantly do the impossible, the pressure to compete, the pressure to be it all - to do it all - it overwhelmed me.

I was an over achiever.

I became a victim of my own passions.

Then, five years after marrying Remy, at twenty-nine years old, I discovered I was pregnant.

No, it was not planned. Yes, it was horrible timing.

I am the first born Canadian in my family.

My whole family is British and my husband's is Scottish and French. For as long as I can remember, I wanted to go to the British Isles. That year we were finally taking the trip I had been dreaming of and planning since I was a child. I had spreadsheets, and even a database, filled with information on places to stay, tours, attractions, transportation, restaurants and even little things like the best way to get money, or which corner shops carried the best tea cakes. I had researched and organized every last second of the trip.

It was going to be fantastic. The trip of my dreams. I was making sure of it!

Murphy, whoever he is with his stupid law, must think he is really damn funny. I have no idea what I did to him, but he can take his law and stuff it. Murphy's law sucks. Because he was right. Everything that can go wrong, will go wrong.

Surprise!

Two days before we were supposed to leave, I realized, in that way that feels like you have been hit by a semi when you were looking the other way, that my period hadn't arrived. I knew my cycle, it was so regular you could set your clock to it. I was due the week before our departure date. Yet here I was, two days before setting out on a three week adventure, and Aunt Flo had not made her monthly visit.

I was such a jumble of emotions. We hadn't talked seriously about starting a family but I had planned on bringing it up during the trip. I was twenty-nine years old and thought having a baby in my early thirties would be perfect. That day I bought a pregnancy test kit, and the next morning I peed on the stick.

A bright blue plus sign appeared.

I sat on the toilet, shaking. Shock would be an understatement. My best friend had been struggling with infertility for years. After many rounds of unsuccessful fertility treatments, they had recently turned to adoption in an attempt to start their family. I could not understand how I had become pregnant. Well I knew *how*, but how could it have happened so easily for us when my best friend struggled? It should have been harder.

For some reason that was the one thought that kept going through my head: *It should have been harder. It's not supposed to be this easy.*

Well the hard parts were there, they were just coming later in the story.

I had crawled out of bed really early to do the test, and it was agonizing waiting for my husband to get up. When he finally staggered out of the bedroom, his eyes still bleary, I told him. A kind wife might have waited until he had woken up a bit more, perhaps after his morning shower or coffee. But I was pregnant and we were about to leave on a three week trip. There was no time for kindness; it was time for shock and awe. It took a few minutes for what I said to sink in. I am not sure it helped that I had the giggles by this point. It just seemed so unreal.

Remy insisted I go to the doctor, immediately. We had to know for sure before we traveled. So off I went to the clinic, only hours before our red eye flight to Heathrow. The doctor sent me to the lab for a pregnancy test, requesting a rush on the results.

Three hours before our flight, moments before heading out the door, the doctor's office had still not called me back. I called them. The obnoxiously polite lady on the phone insisted she could not divulge information over the phone. I pleaded and sweet talked, telling her about our imminent flight, and finally she caved. With a conspiratorial whisper into the handset she said, "Congratulations, you're pregnant."

I am a very open person - just in case you couldn't tell that, from the fact that I have written this book. When my parents drove us to the airport it was so painful not telling them but I knew we had to keep it a secret. At that point we were still trying to wrap our brains around the fact that there was a baby coming. I felt like I was watching everything as an outsider. An outsider who was laughing at how insane it was that I was pregnant. I was going to have a baby. Me!

On the third day of our trip, while staying in London during a heat wave, the morning sickness hit. I have to say, if you are going to vomit in a public loo, as the Brits like to call it, the Harrods' toilets are absolutely the best place to do it.

All my carefully laid plans were trashed. We missed attractions. We canceled tours. I struggled to do even the simplest physical activities. I was completely exhausted. The trip was not horrible, not in the least, but it was not the dream trip I had envisioned and spent years planning.

This was my first brush with the fact that I was no longer in control. Someone else had taken charge. But I still didn't realize what was coming, or how drastically life would change. Can anyone really know how parenthood will affect their lives… and bodies? It is so different for every woman, every family. I have come to see motherhood like a set of pruning shears, and I am simply the tree that is being pruned and shaped by the sharp edges of mothering. I may not have liked some of the cuts, and at times they were incredibly painful, but with time I have grown fuller and more beautiful with each snip.

By the end of the trip the morning sickness had passed, and I was beyond excited about the pregnancy. I thought this was exactly what I needed - a change of pace, a new passion. What could be greater than having a family? Not to mention the generously gifted one year maternity leave from the Canadian government! One whole year off work? Cha-ching! At twenty-nine years old I had hit the over achiever jackpot. This was exactly what I needed to find a new balance in life.

I thought the year off would give me a vacation from my very stressful life and career. I pictured my maternity leave as a time when I could have a change of scenery and recharge my batteries. My time would be spent cuddling my baby, between reading, and perhaps, learning how to cook. After the one year leave I had every intention of returning to the workforce, renewed and ready to do battle once again. After all, I was my career and my passions. I was not going to be one of those women who loses everything once a baby enters the scene. Nope. Not me.

Ever heard of someone being in denial and delusional? So yeah, that was me. That was then. Before POP.

The Expectant Glow

True to form, my pregnancy instantly became my new obsession. I studied; I read so many books and joined online message boards. I learned; joined prenatal groups, took classes, and even attended attachment and breastfeeding support meetings. I trained; I hit the gym every day, I walked and hiked for hours, and I did yoga. I trained for my delivery like I was training for a marathon.

Throughout my pregnancy I kept an open mind about the delivery. I preferred the idea of a drug free, natural delivery, but I was also ready for anything. Or so I thought. I trusted my body to do what billions of women's bodies have done forever, and I trusted that our medical system would step in if my body ran into problems.

The Canadian medical system has its strengths, but it also has its weaknesses. I did not have a great family doctor and, due to an extreme shortage of doctors where we lived, it was not possible to switch to a different doctor. Many families were struggling to get by without a dedicated family doctor, forced to visit medi-clinics for their medical care. I was lucky to have a dedicated family doctor, even if I didn't like her.

Once my pregnancy had been confirmed yet again, she referred me to an OBGYN without consulting me or providing me with any options. It was a take it or leave it situation. I did some asking around and was relieved when the OBGYN came highly recommended by some friends, and friends of friends.

I met with the OBGYN at around week twelve of my pregnancy. She seemed nice enough, as doctors go, but it felt like an assembly line of women, rolling in and out, every time I entered her office. The goal seemed to move as many women through the clinic as possible every single day. The waiting room was constantly crammed, every seat filled with heavily swollen women, while other, less swollen, women stood or leaned against the walls, just trying to take some weight from their feet.

This was supposed to be my special time; I didn't want to be just another number, another butt on those scratchy, ugly brown chairs in the waiting room. Or worse yet, being forced to stand, wobbling from foot to foot as I waited an eternity for my name to be called.

On that first visit, still small and slender, I stood with Remy at my side, subtly checking out all the women in the room. I wondered how far along they were and if it was really as uncomfortable as some of them were making it look.

Then I was called into the examination room. The doctor did a quick check of my vitals and asked if I had any questions. I didn't. Except perhaps why her waiting room was so crowded and unwelcoming, but I kept my mouth shut.

Then she squirted some cold stuff on my belly and squished a handheld device into it. The best noise in the world filled the room. My concerns were completely forgotten the second I heard that rapid thuddity, thuddity, thuddity of my baby's heart. This OBGYN was suddenly the greatest doctor in the world! Obviously that was why her waiting room was so busy. She was the best. I smiled up at Remy, our wet eyes wide with wonder. The doctor smiled, told us everything looked great, then turned and left, leaving Remy and I to our gooey, smiley selves.

The OBGYN had won me over. All she had to do was introduce me to my baby's heartbeat. Yes, I was a cheap win in my hormonal state.

Things were wonderful; the world was a twinkling shiny place for the next few weeks as we announced our big news to the world, then it was time for my twenty week ultrasound and the shine suddenly looked tinny and fake.

I had been booked in for a complete ultrasound plus 3D, which was the newest and greatest technology at the time. I waited anxiously for the appointment. I was going to see my baby for the first time!

My appointment was at the end of the day. So, after a full day at work, we raced across town to the ultrasound clinic. Only one problem, they had no record of my appointment. The lady at the desk assured me they did not want to reschedule as I suggested, instead they would squeeze me in. I didn't want to be squeezed in. This was supposed to be a special moment for Remy and I, and our baby!

But they refused to listen. Insisting they had to do it right then and there.

Including the time spent dealing with the appointment screw up and my ultrasound, I was in and out of the office in less than fifteen minutes.

Fifteen minutes!

There was no 3D, there was no chance to watch my baby move. She turned the monitor toward me for about thirty seconds, showing me a grainy, still image of my baby. She also claimed my due date was a full week earlier than I knew it was. I am not dumb, I know exactly when I got pregnant, but nope, she refused to believe me. I was given three tiny snap shots and sent on my way.

I complained to my OBGYN. She ignored me. I begged for another ultrasound. How could they know if everything really was okay when she had spent less than a minute looking at my baby? I knew the new due date was wrong. I told her over and over again that I knew exactly when I got pregnant. There was only one possible time it could have happened.

Nope, no way, no how, my OBGYN refused to allow me to have another ultrasound. At the time, our medical system did not have any private care options. So, if my doctor refused, I had no other options. I simply could not get an ultrasound.

This was the first glimpse of how my OBGYN was not the great doctor others had proclaimed her to be. I can say that now, it has been confirmed by a professional third party. Those friends who recommended her? Yeah, they all spat out their babies in fifteen minutes flat, from a good, sturdy, practical childbearing pelvis.

My first lesson on childbirth: ask for references from women who have had horrible pregnancies, filled with complications, yet still rave about their OBGYN. Don't listen to the ones who could have done it on their own.

I wanted a different OBGYN, but with our wonderful Canadian medical system it would have taken three months or longer to get a referral to a different OBGYN, so changing part way through my pregnancy was not an option, even if I could have convinced my family doctor to make the referral, which was highly unlikely.

At that time, midwives were also not an option unless you wanted to birth in your own home and it was not yet a regulated industry. The idea of birthing at home, in my own bed, freaked me out. Where I lived, people had their babies in hospitals, it was just how it was done. Little did I know that within a few years things would change dramatically and home births, tub births, and midwife assisted births, would become widely available.

But I dealt with what I had at the time and had faith that things would work out. Millions of women give birth every year, and they all made it through just fine. Right?

Sure, I was not the biggest fan of my OBGYN but she was just a temporary fixture in my life. It would all work out fine.

My naivety and blind faith was absolute. Well at least in the beginning.

The Accident

My pregnancy went fairly smoothly, barring snarky ultrasound technicians, until twenty-four weeks when I was driving to work, early one dark morning. As I cruised down the highway, another car merged onto the road, crossing two lanes of traffic, straight into the side of my vehicle. My car spun around wildly in circles before finally coming to a steaming rest at the side of the highway. It was four days before Christmas.

At the hospital, they only cared about my baby. And, truth be told, that was my main concern at the time too. Even when my OBGYN came to the hospital, she didn't examine me. She only watched the monitors strapped around my softly swelling abdomen, that echoed with a thudding heartbeat that faded in and out as my tiny baby sharked around inside of me. I spent a day in the hospital followed by the next two weeks (over the Christmas holidays) on 'miscarriage watch'. How horrible of a term is that? Thankfully, I did not miscarry.

Did anyone check in with me? Did my doctor call to see how I was doing? Nope. I was on my own.

After the hospital stay the pain hit, hard. My whole left side hurt and, terrified of hurting my unborn baby, I was unwilling to take any medication. I didn't want to do anything that might be unsafe for my baby. I went to my family doctor and she said the ligaments on that side of my abdominal cavity had all been stretched and strained due to the force placed on my body as the car spun out of control. The extra weight of my uterus added to the force exerted by the crash, and increased the amount of damage.

After the Christmas holidays I went to see my OBGYN. I begged her for another ultrasound, absolutely certain that she could not say no after the accident.

What did she say?

You got it. "Nope."

Once again I brought up the fact that the due

date she was working with was wrong. I told her all the dirty details this time, hoping to persuade her to understand. I am a detail focused person.

One of the things I obsessed about was my cycle. Due to a stomach issue, I was unable to take oral birth control, so instead we relied on condoms. Well, feeling all lovey dovey after a wedding, things happened and a certain thing was forgotten. Something we never did. We were religious about our use of protection. But that one day we didn't because I thought we would be still in a safe window, and guess what?

Surprise!

I knew my cycle. I knew when I got pregnant, down to the minute. I knew my actual due date. And I knew the specialist was wrong. What worried me the most was that the ultrasound tech was claiming I was exactly one week farther along than I knew I was. This concerned me for two reasons. One, it meant my baby was big. Two, my doctor was already talking about inducing me on the ultrasound technician's due date if I had not gone into labor naturally by that day. I did not want to be induced. I wanted to have my baby on its proper due date.

So, between that and the car accident, I was very nervous and really wanted another ultrasound to help put my mind at ease. Once again, there was no way, no how, that OBGYN was giving me a second ultrasound. She could not have cared less about my concerns or the crappy experience I had during my first ultrasound. She said the technician had reported that she had seen everything and had no concerns. So no second ultrasound for me.

Have I mentioned my OBGYN was not my favorite person?

You know those fancy ultrasound places you can go to, on your own, now? The private clinics where you pay them to do the ultrasound and they give you videos of your baby sharking about in your belly? I wish those had been around when I was pregnant. I would have been the first customer through the door.

As my due date approached I started getting nervous about the size of my baby. I have a very slender and petite build, with narrow hips. I started out barely showing but, through the last few months of my pregnancy, I swear, I gained at least an inch around my belly every day. I was terrified my baby would be huge. Plus, I was still worried about possible complications from the accident, either for me or the baby. Due to pain from my injuries following the accident I had been forced to give up a lot of my fitness activities, as even the smallest impact caused my ever growing belly to bounce and move painfully.

So, once again, I asked for an ultrasound

during my last trimester. Other pregnant friends were getting ultrasounds during their final trimester, so I thought my request would easily be granted.

Yeah, you know what she said.

During my pregnancy I attended many prenatal courses and expectant mom groups. I studied and learned everything I could about my pregnancy, what was happening to my body, and what would happen during the delivery. Not once did anyone mention the risk of pelvic organ prolapse. The closest I came to uncovering this secret curse of mothers was at a house warming party for a friend. She had teenaged children and was a paramedic.

As we were preparing to leave she grabbed my arm and pulled me to the side. “Are you doing a C-section? Ask for a C-section. You don’t want to know what a vaginal birth will do to your body!” I stood there, silently stunned at her comment, then my husband called and we were on our way. Thoughts raced through my mind as I tried to understand what she had said. All I could think was that I was young, fit and women had been having babies forever. Our bodies were made for this. Of course I was going to do things naturally. Why would I opt for surgery? It seemed very extreme, very out of left field, and very, very weird.

I quickly forgot her comment that day and

moved on, probably to eat something. I ate a lot at that point in my pregnancy. But after I delivered my baby, her words would echo through my mind daily.

As my due date drew closer, I argued and pleaded with the OBGYN, finally putting my foot down firmly. I did not want to be induced on the date provided by the ultrasound technician. Finally she agreed with one concession from me. I had to go to the hospital for an ultrasound exactly one week after the ultrasound tech's due date. Which, coincided with the date I believed to be my proper due date. If the ultrasound revealed any concerns, I would be induced immediately. I happily agreed. For once I felt heard, even if it was in a small way.

Finally, on the due date I had predicted, I went into labor. I never did make it to that ultrasound. My contractions started the night before and by 4am we were driving to the hospital.

It was a crazy drive. We had rehearsed and planned our route to the hospital but, of course, on the big day we came across a police barricade. The road was closed, no one was getting through, and the police were not letting anyone turn back. The police were telling everyone to park and wait.

But my baby was not waiting. My

contractions were less than five minutes apart. Remy was actually pretty chuffed that he got to use the, 'but my wife's in labor' line. The cops quickly allowed our car through the barricades so we could take a side road to the hospital.

Even though I had visions of birthing in the car, it turned out that we didn't need to rush. I still had hours to go until my baby would finally arrive in a grand fashion.

Not once during my pregnancy did my doctor talk to me about my choices or risks. She never asked if I had a family history of delivery complications. She definitely never mentioned prolapse complications. And she never talked to me about the risks or options of vaginal vs C-section birth. I believe, had these conversations taken place, my life would have turned out very differently. And never having gone through a pregnancy before, I did not know what questions to ask.

Well, it was too late for questions or options now. It was show time!

The End Goal

When a woman is pregnant, the labor is often seen as the end-line or end goal. In fact, I think no matter how a child comes into a family, it can be hard for parents, and those around them, not to focus on the arrival of the child as the goal. Holding onto some sort of belief that things will work themselves out when the little one arrives. I find this especially true when I talk to families that have struggled to add a child to their family, whether through fertility issues or the adoption process.

As someone who has grown my family through pregnancy and adoption (Oops, spoilers!), I can tell you, no matter how a child comes to a family, no matter how hard the journey to their arrival seems, sometimes it's the part after the arrival that is the hardest! And sometimes, it's for reasons you would never have predicted.

As I went into labor, things were progressing well. In fact I did not find the pain too much to bear. It was intense. Damn it was intense. Every contraction would force my body to fold in half, frozen, unable to move until it passed. But I was coping. I was doing okay. All that training, studying and preparing was paying off. I was laughing in the face of pain. Giddy with excitement. I was ready to get this show on the road and meet my baby!

After about ten hours of labor, I started vomiting with each contraction, every three to five minutes. It was horrible. When you are in labor you cannot eat or drink, so I was dry heaving until the pain from the dry heaving was overshadowing anything that was happening to the rest of my body.

I finally begged the nurse for anything to stop the vomiting. She suggested an epidural and I immediately said, "Hell yes!" I would have said yes to a club to the head too, but whatever; a woman in labor should not be held accountable for what she says, hence why these things should be discussed *before* contractions begin!

They also gave me something to speed up my delivery. At that point I had been in labor for over fourteen hours. After the medications had been administered, as a new nurse was helping me into the bed, she told me she could have given me some anti-nausea medications and then proceeded to guilt me for taking an epidural, telling me, with a shake of her head, "You could have done it without the meds."

I am not sure if her comment was because she was disappointed in me for taking the drugs or the other nurses for immediately suggesting an epidural rather than the anti-nausea meds. Either way, I was not in the mood for her comments at that moment. Things were not proceeding the way I had envisioned during all those months of planning and preparation. I was getting a little stressed out and anxious, plus, as soon as I was stretched out on the bed, yet another nurse examined me and announced that my baby was stuck and positioned wrong. She then proceeded to reach inside me with her hands and tried to turn my baby.

I found out afterward that she was wrong. My baby was positioned properly. What she thought was his nose was actually the back of his head, where the plates of his head had compressed to fit down the birth canal. The plates had overlapped a bit and the nurse had mistaken this bump for my baby's nose. I also discovered she could have seriously hurt my baby and me doing this. At the time, of course, I knew nothing. Only that I wanted to meet my baby already.

I finally started pushing and after an hour of pushing (and still feeling each contraction but unable to move to cope with the pain, thanks to an ineffective epidural!), my OBGYN announced that my baby was stuck and in distress. We needed to get him out now! The doctor turned and walked away, returning moments later with a contraption that I still have nightmares about… the giant, metal forceps.

I asked her if she could please do an emergency C-section?

Nope, it was too late.

We had been at this for fifteen hours and now, suddenly, she was in a rush? I had barely seen her throughout my labor. She had stopped in only twice, for less than five minutes. How could we suddenly be in such a desperate situation? It made no sense to my exhausted brain.

I asked if there was anything else she could use.

Or if there was anything else I could do.

Nope, too late.

She then proceeded to clamp that archaically nasty contraption on my baby's head, that was still well inside my vagina, before I had a chance to take a breath and process what she was saying.

I am a redhead and therefore a bleeder. In my early twenties I got my belly button pierced. I went to the best piercing artist in the city. She assured me that belly buttons were straight forward. "No one ever bleeds… unless, of course, you are a redhead," she added as she pierced my skin and quickly started padding my whole stomach with gauze to soak up the pooling blood. Even after I left the piercing studio my belly button continued to bleed on and off for hours. It has become a trusted fact about my body, if there is a chance of bleeding, trust that I will gush like a geyser. It is the joy of being a fair-skinned redhead.

My baby's entrance into the world was like a scene from a horror flick. That room should have been draped in plastic. They ripped my baby from my body. No preparation, nothing. The OBGYN braced both feet on the legs of the bed, leaned back and yanked him from my body.

Tearing delicate tissues to shreds.

I had fourth degree tearing, which is as bad as it sounds. The doctor made sure my baby was healthy before squatting down between my legs and stitching me up. Not much was said to me at this point; my job was done and everyone was focused on the baby or stitching me up. My head was of no importance, so it was ignored. No one said anything about how much damage was done to my body, and although that epidural was lame, it did numb things enough that the pain was not too intense at that point. I was blissfully unaware what had happened down there.

A short time later, while we were enjoying our first cuddles with our baby, an 8lb 8oz baby boy we named Jace, a nurse came over and pressed on my belly. Blood shot out of me and across the room, splattering into the wall. The nurse paled, then without looking at us, ran from the room.

Moments later the OBGYN came into the room, did her own push-splatter test, then ordered the nurses to put special medications into my IV. With a laugh, and pat on my shoulder, she said, "Oh, the joys of being a redhead." As if the spectacular blood loss was my fault and had nothing to do with what she had just done to my body. Then she turned and left. If I hadn't been so befuddled by my gorgeous baby I would have torn her to shreds. But his gorgeous blue eyes and dark spiky hair with blond tips had me completely besotted. Nothing else in the world mattered anymore.

It was not the delivery I expected. But it was over. We had survived. The journey was over, we were at the end goal. He was here! Now he was in our arms, everything would be fine. Or so I thought.

PART 2

DIAGNOSIS

The Beginning

The next few hours were a whirlwind, so many people came to visit us at the hospital. I was hurting and so uncomfortable. And bleeding. I am not sure what medication the doctor gave me shortly after delivery to help with the bleeding, but from my point of view it was not working. I was soaking through sanitary napkin after sanitary napkin. They had my bed padded and had to change it constantly as I soaked through over and over again. It was especially hard having so many visitors. I was embarrassed and uncomfortable, sitting in a pool of my own blood, as I tried to entertain and chat about Jace. I plastered an 'I'm a glowing, happy new mother' smile on my face, while I tried to hide what was my body was doing under the blankets.

That night I stayed in the hospital with Jace. Remy was sent home as the room did not have anywhere he could sleep comfortably. Years earlier he had been in a really bad car accident that left him with a debilitating, permanent back injury. The original plan was to stay in one of the special birthing suites that had a queen sized bed, so Remy could stay and help me with the baby. Of course, once we got to the hospital, they claimed all the suites were unavailable. Remy had to fight just to get me a private room.

He has always been my knight in shining armor, out to protect me and our family.

My first night as a mother was not at all what I had envisioned through all those long months as my stomach swelled. I was still bleeding like crazy and I could not sit up, the pain 'down there' was worse than any labor contraction. They had left my bed raised and even being at an angle was painful, as it put pressure on swollen, bruised tissues. The only way to get any relief was to curl up on my side. When I buzzed the nurses, asking for help, they brushed me off. Refused to come. At one point, Jace was crying in his crib beside the bed. I tried to stand but could not get up. Any movement sent lightning bolts of pain tearing through my body. I started crying as well. Less than a day into motherhood and already I was a complete failure. My baby was crying and I couldn't do anything about it.

Yes, I was having a pity party. I am not sure how long it lasted but after getting some tears out I felt a little stronger.

Wiping away my tears I rolled onto my hip, determined to do whatever was needed for my baby. I had an idea. "Hang on, Jace, Mom's coming!" I said as I stretched one arm into the crib. The nurses had swaddled him tightly, so I grabbed a fistful of blankets with one hand, then with a deep breath rolled him up and over to the edge of the crib. There I was able to reach him with my other hand and lift him up and into the bed with me.

I lay there, panting and gasping for breath, absolutely elated. I had done it.

I snuggled Jace up beside me, breathing in his beautiful new baby smell. The pain was momentarily forgotten, or at least ignored, for more important things: new baby smell, the most intoxicating scent known to women.

We slept cuddled together for the rest of the night. My nose buried in his head of thick, dark, sweet smelling hair, listening to each of his precious breaths. It was pure bliss.

The next day I insisted on going home immediately. I needed to get away from that horrible hospital. I felt that if I could flee the 'scene of the crime', everything would be fine. I would heal up and life would return to normal. It was all the doctor's fault, and the damn hospital, where all these people viewed me as nothing more than a number, an inconvenience in their day. No one at the hospital cared about my bleeding or pain. So why stay there?

I just needed to get home. To be alone with my husband and baby. There I would be okay. Things would go back to normal.

We had our baby! We had reached the end goal.

And that was all that mattered. Everything would be fine now.

Or, at least I hoped.

The Unglamorous Mother

It hurt. Labor was nothing compared to the pain I dealt with for weeks after my son's birth. For the first week I could not sit, I literally had to roll everywhere. Which was damn difficult because my boobs swelled to double Gs. No, that was not a typo. When I went to the bra specialist, they could not fit me. My boobs were enormous. And hot, and hard. Yes, I was engorged.

When I went to see the community nurse for help, she shrieked… well okay, she didn't shriek, but horror would accurately describe her reaction. Then she ran off, coming back moments later with a hospital breast pump and instructions to use it to help drain excess milk.

"But don't use it too much! Otherwise you could increase production even more!" she admonished, as she ushered me out the door with a motherly clucking sound.

I threw away gallons of milk after my freezer reached capacity and Remy complained we had no room left for adult food anymore. We had an on-going joke that I could have fed half of the world's orphans. The irony of this joke was not lost on me, a couple of years later, when we went to Ethiopia.

There was no 'new mother glow' for me. I was the engorged on top, shredded down below woman. Motherhood was far from rosy.

It was over a month before I could sit even remotely like a human being. Instead I had to prop myself up on a hip, twisting my spine so all my weight was balanced over one hip bone.

I broke down sobbing from the pain so many times I lost count. Normally I am tough - really tough. I laugh when I'm hurt; weird but true, the more I hurt the more I laugh. Even during labor (between the vomit), I laughed.

I once had half of my index finger chewed off by a rat during a psychology lab experiment in university. My rat, who I had nicknamed Mickie, did not feel chocolate was payment enough for running mazes, he wanted human flesh! After he ate my finger we renamed him Zombie Mickey.

At the hospital, I laughed hysterically. The doctor thought I had completely lost it as he tried to clean the ragged wound. I laugh in the face of pain. But not this time. Nothing had ever hurt like those first few weeks after Jace's delivery.

Due to the tearing, I had to flush and care for my stitches, which meant I immediately became intimately familiar with how different things were 'down there'. On top of the delay in my bodily functions returning to normal, things down there were very swollen and raw. When I did go to the toilet, I had to use a squirt bottle filled with warm water and flush myself as I passed urine. I learned quickly to use tons of warm water. It burned like the hottest of fires down there if I got lax with the water.

One time, and only one time, I didn't have a filled bottle waiting beside the toilet. Warm water was best, but water of any temperature was better than nothing. Sometimes there was no way I could fill a bottle with warm water. Once the fountain was ready to start, it would go with no warning and no control from me!

Anyway, what kind of ninja bladder can resist the sound of water, especially a full bladder? In that first week I had my first experience with not making it to the toilet in time, followed by a number of close calls. My bladder had definitely lost all of its ninja skills following the birth.

So I kept a squirt bottle always at the ready and, for that first month, stayed locked away in my home. Just me, my baby, and my engorged boobs and raw lady parts. Fun times!

But not just raw, things were swollen and loose. I kept expecting things to tighten up, for all the weird bulges and swellings to go away. But they didn't.

After birth it takes time for bowel movements to return to normal, but the first time I tried to have a proper bowel movement I could feel the stool pushing against skin. Horrified, I was convinced the doctor had sewn me up all wrong. She had put my poop hole in the wrong place! Tentatively, after ensuring the door was locked, I actually checked to ensure she *had* left a hole. Thank goodness there was still a hole there, but it seemed to be about half an inch away from where my body thought it should be. I was convinced she had sewn me up wrong!

I was so embarrassed; how do you bring that up in polite conversation?

"So, you know when the doctor was stitching me up? Well, the funniest thing, she forgot to put my anus back where it should be! Hilarious! Can you pass the biscuits please?"

Awkward!

So yeah, I kept that little gem to myself. I discovered by wriggling around on the toilet and sitting in weird positions I could pass stool. Was it normal and right? Nothing seemed normal anymore. Nothing was all right. I had no idea what was happening to my body.

At my six week postpartum check-up, I demanded to know what was wrong with me. The OBGYN said everything looked great and that, with time, any issues should resolve themselves.

"Childbirth is a very traumatic process. Your body needs time to recover. Give your body a year and everything should be back to normal." Then the evil doctor started swooning over my baby and really, when someone swoons over your spawn, it distracts you from your purpose. Because *of course* your baby is the cutest baby on the planet, and definitely a keeper, and the best thing to ever happen. This doctor was the master of distraction.

So, by default of baby swooning distractions, I decided to trust her. I had time. I had another ten months until I had to return to work. Lots of time for things to fix themselves up. And look at the beautiful baby I got for all my trouble! Well worth the price!

Well except when it never should have happened, and the 'price' could have been prevented. But I didn't know that at the time. This troubling knowledge would come later.

Life was good; I was ready to give my body time. Then Remy and I tried to have sex about eight weeks after Jace was born. It was like shooting ping pong balls down a hallway, things were so loose. Nothing moved. Nothing hurt either. Not that first time; the pain was a nasty surprise about a month later.

Over time, pain during sex became a constant. The rest of my body was happy to go, but inside there was pain. With some experimentation, we found certain positions that did not cause pain, but it was frustrating. Every session was full of constant questions.

"Does that hurt?"

"Nope, is that good for you?"

"Yup, what about this?"

"Ouch, ow, not there!"

I just wanted to relax and get it on again. To be lost in passion, consumed by desire. Living in the moment, drowning in pleasurable sensations. I wanted it to be the way it used to be.

Pain and prolapse took that from me. From Remy too.

I breastfed my son - how could I not with so much bounty on tap? It was three months before the engorging subsided and I shrank down to a men's magazine approved 32DD. Throughout most of that time I lived in tank tops and yoga pants. Thank goodness yoga clothing was cool! I was rocking the new trends, but it wasn't because I wanted to be the cool mom; well not totally... maybe a small part of me still dreamed of being one of the cool kids.

Nope, I did it because every bra felt like a torture device and pants are made with these really annoying seams through the crotch. Yoga clothes were comfortable and forgiving; oh, and one day Remy said they made my ass look good.

That night I bought three more pairs.

Since I was breastfeeding, my cycle did not return for over nine months. Even before the return of my cycle, I still felt like something was wrong. Something was not the way it should be. I went online (yeah internet!), and found a lot of women talking about their bodies changing after childbirth, but the advice was always to give it time - it would get better.

Why so much time? And why, oh why, did all the other moms seem so happy and carefree, playing with their babies at the park, going on mom and baby adventures, and joining baby bootcamps?

Oh, the bootcamps. One day, when Jace was three months old, I decided the way to fix things was to get back in shape.

And Then My Uterus Fell Out

And then my uterus fell out. Well not all the way out, or this would be a really short story. And it didn't happen suddenly, but instead, bit by bit, things fell and things changed for the worse. Altering the course of my life.

I had always been really fit. As time progressed after my delivery, and it seemed like I was only losing more control over my body, rather than improving, I convinced myself that if I could just get fit again everything would return to normal. Other moms in all my mommy groups were doing it, so of course I figured this was what I needed for my recovery.

In fact, I was getting so scared at that point I would have tried pretty much anything to get my body back. Working out just seemed like a logical solution. Get fit, get healthy, and your body will be strong and whole. It sounded good on paper.

I signed up for Mom and Baby Aquasize, Stroller Bootcamp and Mommy and Me Yoga. I wanted to get fit. Now. Hard and fast. I was ready to get my life back. I was excited. I had so much hope.

I lasted three classes into the bootcamp. They kept making me do squats, while walking and pushing my stroller, then breaking into wind sprints, then stopping and lifting weights. Not once did the instructors look at my form, or ensure what I was doing was actually safe for my postpartum body. No one asked if I had suffered any trauma during the birth. I quickly realized my physical safety was not in knowledgeable hands in that class (a very disturbing trend, in postnatal classes, I discovered). As things down there became more and more painful after each class, I eventually dropped out.

Aquasize was better. Being in water meant that all the pressure and pain down there was relieved a bit. However, I forgot to consider the fact that I don't swim. Scratch that, I am *terrified* of water. As soon as my personal flotation devices - aka boobs - were submerged as we moved into deeper water, I would go into a full blown panic attack.

Despite my fears, the relief from the pain and pressure made it worth toughing out. I successfully completed the whole session of Aquasize, by always finding a reason to stay in the shallow end of the pool.

Oops, I just need to come over here and adjust my swimsuit, you go on ahead.

Oh, heading to the deep end? Give me a moment, I think Jace might have a little surprise in his nappy.

And on and on. I am sure everyone thought I was crazy, but it was worth it to have some pain free exercise.

It was around that time I started becoming the queen of excuses. Usually completely made up ones, as I tried to mask the shameful truth of my body's failings.

Yoga, my dearly beloved yoga. I knew that program, with its no impact, gentle stretching style of exercise, would be perfect for me. It started out beautifully. I felt amazing after the relaxing, easy-going classes. The asanas were designed to promote attachment and bonding with baby, and the other mothers were not frantic fitness freaks like the bootcamp moms. I had found my place and was sure fitness and healing were around the corner.

One day, we did a sun salutation. I started confidently, stretching deeply into the back bend. Enjoying the feeling of freedom and strength as I opened my heart and chest. As I bent forward it happened. My fanny farted. Loudly.

It was horrific. I pretended it wasn't me. Giving the baby beside Jace the eye as if he had made that awful noise… of course I didn't blame my baby - that would just be mean!

Despite my stealth and deflection attempts I could feel my redheaded complexion ratting me out as I flushed hotly.

I continued through the movements, keeping my fanny as tightly clenched as I possibly could, until the instructor came over. With gentle hands she corrected my posture and whispered in my ear, "Now just relax into the movement. Trust your body."

Obviously she had not heard what my body had done earlier.

Sadly, that was not my last fanny fart. I became the master of throat clearing just as my fanny would decide to demand some attention. My goal was simple, to mask the sound and maintain some level of dignity. I loved yoga so much. I didn't want to stop but then I noticed the pressure. As I would move certain ways, the pressure down there would increase to painful levels. One day, I intentionally took the far back corner of the room for my mat.

There was something I needed to check and I

didn't want everyone to see what I was doing.

As we went into one of the moves that caused me pain I reached down and gently ran a hand along my crotch. I could feel things bulging and swelling down there.

That night I did the same move in the bathroom, but with a mirror. Staring back at me was my cervix, protruding from my body. Using my fingers I pushed things back inside and vowed never to do yoga again.

I reminded myself what the doctor and all those internet voices had said. Things will get better with time. I repeated the mantra to myself all day, every day. Willing myself to get better, like all those other women.

But mine never 'got better'. The weird bulges and swellings stayed. The difficulty on the toilet, and sometimes not getting to the toilet in time, remained. And yes, the pain continued. I was in constant pain and discomfort.

Looking back, I now know this was when the grief and depression started. I would attend Mommy and Baby classes and all the moms looked so happy and carefree, playing with their babies. Their labors forgotten, as so many people had promised. For me, I couldn't forget. I had constant pain as a reminder of my son's arrival into this world.

At around ten months postpartum, my cycle came back and it was obvious things were really 'not right'! I tried to insert a tampon and it shot out like a bullet into the toilet.

I called the OBGYN in a panic and her nurse diagnosed me, *over the phone,* with pelvic organ prolapse. I asked if I should come in and was told, with a giggle, "No, no, you need to go to a specialist!"

Thankfully, I never had to see or talk to them again.

I hung up and called Remy, sobbing uncontrollably.

Pelvic organ prolapse was a secretly whispered phrase I had only heard a few times throughout my life. No one had ever talked openly about the subject. None of my friends. None of my sex ed teachers. None of the nurses teaching prenatal classes. No one.

Like a forbidden, shameful topic it was discussed in hushed voices and quick references. The sudden need to pee. Jokes about not being able to jump on a trampoline. Or the hushed disappearance of women going for hysterectomies, the reason never shared.

I knew almost nothing about POP, but what I did know was that it was something to fear, something to be shamed by.

So I cried. A lot.

The Therapist With the Purple Vibrator

I honestly believed, in that moment when I was diagnosed with POP over the phone, that my life would never be the same. And you know what? It hasn't been.

Somehow, I was given an appointment to see the specialist less than a week after the phone call. This was unheard of, and I still have no idea how it happened; even the specialist said the wait was normally well over a year. I believe the receptionist at my OBGYN office pulled some strings for me, but I never questioned the good fortune. I was just happy that I was getting medical help immediately.

The specialist was actually a very nice elderly nurse, who made clucking noises at how young

I was. She let it slip that my OBGYN was their number one referring doctor, known for not taking care with women's bodies and being much too fond of the forceps.

The kindly nurse examined me for about twenty minutes. Lying down, standing up; she had me cough and bear down. Finally, with a snap of her latex gloves, she pronounced that I had a particularly severe case of prolapse, with extensive scarring plus nerve and muscle damage.

Officially, I was diagnosed with a severe stage 3/4 cystocele (fancy word for bladder prolapse), severe stage 4 uterine prolapse and moderate stage 2 rectocele (fancy word for rectal prolapse). In easy-speak, my bladder and uterus had made a bid for freedom when my son had been born by attempting to flee my body with him toward the bright lights. My rectum had also started to flee, but thankfully did not make it very far. With a shake of her greying curls, and more sympathetic clucking, she told me there was no natural way for my organs to return to their proper place. Pelvic organ prolapse could not be cured without surgery.

My body - the body that I had worked so hard on for years - had failed. Not just a fail, but an epic fail.

Following that specialist appointment at the Women's Health Clinic, I was referred down the hall to an urogynocology-physiotherapist (urogyn-physio). The goal of physio was to get my pelvic floor muscles functioning again. Jace was ten months old and I was still not able to do a Kegel, an exercise that involved contracting the vaginal and pelvic floor muscles. I needed to get those muscles moving again. Physio would also help with the scar tissue and nerve damage. It sounded good, but it wouldn't fix the prolapses. Nothing could fix those, except surgery. At that point, they were simply trying to help me live with the prolapses, as best as I could, until I became a suitable surgery candidate.

If you don't like your yearly doctor visits, imagine having someone pushing around in there for over an hour, intently searching for those points that cause you the MOST pain. She would ask me intimate questions about my most recent sexual encounters, what position I was in and what I was doing when I experienced pain. Then, once she had located the most painful spots, she would push on them until they went numb. Yeah, just another day of fun in the life a new mother. The things they do not tell you about in prenatal classes!

I was scheduled for physio sessions weekly, for a full year. Half a day, every week. Time I should have been spending with my son, was spent lying exposed, while being probed, instead.

To add insult to injury, I was notified by my employer that they had gone through a series of cutbacks and reorganization. I no longer had a job to return to when my maternity leave ended. With my health issues, and the time commitments with physio, job hunting was impossible. I was forced into being a stay-at-home mom. Something I had never dreamed of becoming.

In less than a year, everything I understood myself to be was gone. I didn't know this new person with the broken body and no goals, beyond somehow getting through another day.

Is it any wonder depression became my constant companion? I tried to focus on the positive. With some shuffling of priorities we were able to live on one income, and with Remy's encouragement I dedicated my time to healing, or at least trying to find a way to cope with my prolapses. It was hard, though; negative thoughts often consumed me. The positives seemed thinly veiled and like false promises. This wasn't what I had envisioned motherhood to be. All I could do was follow Remy's advice and do everything I could to try and heal.

My physiotherapist was a hyperactive lady with short cropped hair and the air of someone that has drunk too much coffee. The appointment would involve the therapist pushing around inside of my vagina for an hour. Her goal was to find trigger points. From my point of view, they were essentially points that hurt like hell when touched. I have no idea what the medical stuff was behind those points, but the therapist said it was like a massage therapist releasing a knot. It was painful while it was being worked on but, once it released, you would feel better. Well, I went for a year, never missed an appointment. She pushed while I squirmed, and I never really did feel better. Sure, the pain subsided a bit but my organs were still hanging low, and that was the issue that haunted me daily.

Every session she would have me try and do Kegels. Nothing ever moved down there. Nothing. Not a twitch. It was as if every muscle down there had disappeared.

I hated being asked to do a Kegel while someone had their fingers in me. It was like facing a chemistry test - I failed every single time. Yet I had no idea how to pass, how to make things better. No matter how hard I tried, I constantly failed. I hated it. I started to hate myself. I was a failure.

As we neared the end of my time with the physiotherapist she decided I should learn how to care for the trigger points myself. So started the most embarrassing and awkward experience of my life. With her fingers pushing around inside me, she talked about how I could put my own fingers in my vagina and push on the trigger points. As we spoke she turned away from me, then spun back holding a purple vibrator. It was one of those angled ones, with the big bulb on the end. She then proceeded to demonstrate, against the outside of her pants, how I could use the vibrator to get to the trigger points and push on them.

With a sly grin, she suggested I should also get my husband to help out.

At the time, I was stunned to silence. Now I want to go back and give that physio a hug and present her with a bouquet of purple vibrators. This condition sucks, but it is not the end. She was trying to give me hope. Make things fun. I can see that now. It took time, distance, and a lot of work, but truly, that woman was a blessing. It could not have been easy, working with depressed, struggling women. How many times had she heard how the sky was falling? Or I guess, in this case, the bladder/uterus/rectum was falling? Either way, the level of panic and anxiety from her patients would have been the same and must have been draining.

Throughout that year in physio, my anger and frustration grew. Why had no one ever talked about this? I took months of prenatal classes and not once was POP, or any of my other complications, mentioned. Everything I read talked about how this condition affects older women. Older women. Since when does thirty years old count, in any way, as older? As time went on, and I learned more, it turned out it was not at all an older person condition. In fact, most of the women reaching out for support on various internet groups were young and pre-menopausal. I felt so alone, and ashamed, but it turns out I was not alone. Not at all. I just needed to be brave enough to step forward and use my voice.

Through my physio sessions I learned to get over my own reservations and shyness. If I wanted to do anything to help myself, I needed to get bold and honest and be willing to talk about anything. Including how to get my husband to massage things down there, to help relieve nerve damage and release tension.

Remember the redheaded thing? Well, not only does that mean I am a bleeder but I also blush like an over-ripe tomato. I spent a lot of time hot under the collar and flushed to the tips of my toes, but somehow I did it. An intense amount of determination and stubbornness, layered on top of a lot of anger and grief, helped me find the strength to talk openly about these things, and to do what I needed to do to find some relief and healing.

At home I was eventually able to find some pressure points myself and apply the proper pressure to release them. This really helped my sex life. It seemed like every time we did it, we would find one of those damn pressure points. I am not into pain with my passion. So it was a massive relief when I was able to start taking back some control over my body, to relieve some of the pain and make one of life's pleasures pleasurable again.

Towards the end of my physio treatments I stopped breastfeeding; Jace was getting close to two years old and we were both ready. I was excited to see if my prolapses would improve. The physiotherapist had mentioned that some women experienced improvement after they stop breastfeeding. In my case, it made no difference; in fact, as Jace was getting bigger my prolapses were getting worse from carrying him. Eventually, I was forced into giving up carrying him. Even with my favorite baby carriers, it was just too much for my body. I started using strollers instead, but my stroller was this big, fancy, brand name thing that I had purchased while pregnant. It had all sorts of gadgets and toys… and it weighed over thirty pounds. I replaced it with an ultra-light, fold up stroller, which helped a bit, but I discovered if I put my purse or any bags on the handles the whole thing would tip over backwards.

Nothing like tipping over your kid in the middle of the mall to draw a lot of judgment filled glances and muttered comments.

It seemed like I just could not win. Life demanded that I be able to lift and carry a lot of weight - my baby, groceries, diaper bags, the shopping. The physiotherapist taught me some techniques in an attempt to limit the pressure on my pelvic floor, but she conceded it was next to impossible with little ones at home. Which was one of the main reasons the surgeons would not consider me for surgery until my children were older.

After a year we parted ways. She wished me the best and said that in a few years, after I had surgery, I should come back to see her again. So instead of goodbye, we said "See you soon."

Sent Into the World

After the urogyn-physio ended our sessions, I was sent back to the kindly nurse at the Women's Health Clinic for a pessary fitting. The first time I was introduced to a pessary, the nurse walked in with what looked like a box filled with bizarre looking blue plastic sex toys. All individually shrink wrapped. The idea is that you insert the device and it holds up the prolapsed tissues and organs. You leave it in all the time, and it helps to relieve pressure and helps with urinary and bowel functioning.

An on-going issue I faced was that when I went pee I would stand up, move around a bit, then need to go again almost immediately. I called it the potty dance and it was annoying as heck. Especially when I was in public washrooms with a toddler who liked to lick everything.

If the pessary would help me with this issue, then I was all for giving it a try.

One problem, I was so severely scarred and prolapsed that the pessaries fell out. Well, except when they were big enough to stay put, but the pain was so severe due to damaged nerves that I couldn't stand up and straighten my back. I was stuck in this bizarre hunchback, twisted up position.

The specialist declared that my vagina was two vastly different sizes, due to the damage sustained during my son's delivery. If she inserted a pessary large enough to stay up on the right hand side, where I was larger, it caused extreme pain on my left hand side, where I was very narrow.

There was nothing they could do. Pessaries and I were simply not meant to be together. So they sent me on my way and said to come back when I was done with children (bio or adopted) because my only option would be surgery. After surgery, I would be limited to not lifting more than twenty pounds for the rest of my life. Due to this, I had to be done with babies or the surgeon would refuse to see me. I had already heard this from the physiotherapist, but it hurt so much more coming from the nurse. It was so final. So absolute.

Once again, I cried. I did not want surgery. The nurse was very clear: they would be taking my uterus as part of the surgery. I did not want a hysterectomy. My uterus worked fine, it was just in the wrong spot. Why would they take a perfectly functioning organ that was still serving a purpose?

I was beginning to feel like I had during my pregnancy and delivery, like the specialists were just steamrolling over me. I was just another body in the endless line of bodies that they administer to every day. There was no special attention or consideration given. No advice on how to survive until surgery, or if there was anything else I could do. I was simply sent out into the world.

At home I tried to adapt to this new body, with all of its aches and pains and limitations. My son was now a stroller baby, even though he was walking at almost two years old; the strain of reaching down to hold his hand, or chasing after him, was too much for my body. If I was taking him out with me, I needed him safely contained.

I stopped going to fitness classes after trying a few more unsuccessfully. I lost all faith in these supposed professionals when not one postnatal instructor had heard of prolapse, and in many cases had never even had a vaginal birth. They were these young, fit, college students, who believed their bodies were invincible.

I left them with their rock hard, invincible bodies and instead opted for long solitary walks, broken up by stops at park benches or playgrounds where I could rest for a bit before continuing.

I felt very lost and very, very alone.

But around this time, something good was starting to come around. Something I am not sure would have ever happened if I had not been through all of these experiences.

I found my second son.

PART 3

FINDING FRUSTRATION AND PERSPECTIVE

One Door Closes

Remember those five year life plans? Well, one of the details in those plans was that I wanted to adopt. I am not sure when I first developed this desire but, on my very first date with Remy, I asked him what he thought about adoption. I can't remember his answer but it must have been a good one. He's still here, after all.

He also gave the right answer when I presented him with a folder about international adoption, about a year after our Jace's birth. A few months after my prolapse diagnosis.

Following my diagnosis I spent about four hours researching pregnancy and prolapse. The results were beyond disheartening. Extremely high risk of miscarriage, extended periods of bed rest required, preterm labor, plus the very real issue that a second pregnancy would likely cause even more damage and lead to things prolapsing even further.

If the idea of repeating the delivery of my first son wasn't enough of a turn off, facing months of bed rest, with a toddler to care for, sealed the deal for me. I was not going to have any more biological children.

The truth was, I still wanted another baby. I just could not fathom the idea of another pregnancy and birth. I was a year postpartum and the pain from, and fear of, my prolapse was still intense. So my original dream of adopting very quickly became our plan for baby number two.

I hate the term 'plan B'. Adoption was definitely not a plan B for us. In fact, adoption had always been my first desire to create a family, but the process to adopt was so foreign and complicated. Without the push from POP (isn't that a type of candy?), I am not sure I would have found the time and drive to navigate the rough waters of the adoption process.

Throughout my twenties my friends and I would often discuss babies, especially as our friends started getting pregnant and starting their own families. Every time the topic came up I would adamantly respond, "Remy and I are adopting. Probably from Africa." My friends would laugh, not believing me.

A few of my close friends were adopted. Their adoptions happened during the seventies and eighties, when adoptions were all domestic, closed door affairs. My friends were all very open when I talked to them about being adopted and, in every case, they encouraged me to follow my dream.

Through my previous job I worked closely with social services and would often find time to visit their websites and read materials about adoption or children waiting for families. I dreamed of the day I would adopt, but never felt the push to realize the dream. Not yet. There were always more courses to take, new exciting projects to tackle, or amazing trips to plan. Children were not a part of the picture. Down the road - yes - but not yet. Then I had Jace, our little surprise baby, followed by my traumatic delivery and life altering diagnosis of prolapse.

I could never have predicted my life story in one of my five year plans. It was too unreal. Too many crazy things had happened. I mean really, my uterus fell out! That was not normal. Adopting, though, was right. No, not right. Perfect. I was so happy I was going to fulfill that one dream, even if it seemed like so many other dreams had been taken from me by POP. Prolapse was the push I needed to pursue that one lifelong desire. I was going to adopt a child from Ethiopia.

The choice in country was actually a very easy one to make. Due to international, federal and provincial regulations, very few countries were available to us. At the time, Ethiopia had a very stable, successful and smooth program. The cost to adopt was scary, but not as scary as the idea going through another traumatic birth.

We filled out the application form and started the exciting, and long, process to adopt.

Sadly, the time waiting to adopt was not a positive one for my prolapse issues, as more and more complications made themselves known.

My periods were the worst time for me. When sitting (or staying stationary in any position for any length of time, including sleeping), the blood would pool behind the tissues. When I eventually moved, it would gush out, soaking through the best feminine products, my clothing and beyond. For years I slept on a towel at that time of month, to protect my mattress. I am not sure why it would vary so much each month, but some months were so bad I even used towels on the chairs and couches.

One day, when Jace was about a year old, I decided to visit my old co-workers to show off my baby. That was what new moms do, right? They go around showing off their babies.

Well I had my period that day. When I left the house it had not seemed too heavy, but as I walked around, visiting with numerous old friends and co-workers, things started getting heavier. I tried to excuse myself to use the washroom, but everyone was stopping us, raving about Jace. As I was sitting in a co-workers office, I gushed. In the space of a breath, blood soaked through all my clothes and onto the chair. I have never been so embarrassed and ashamed in my life. I decided that day I simply could not return to work. There was no way. Physically, I could not do meetings and desk work anymore.

Adoption is not cheap and living on one income was tough enough. Living on one income and paying the huge expenses for an international adoption was not going to work at all.

The pressure to return to work was mounting. I tried to work from home doing odd jobs, selling odd things, but for the amount of hours I put in, the pay was pathetic. I came from a very well paying, high level job. Working for peanuts only added to my feelings of being a failure. I spent a year trying all sorts of work from home jobs, including doing contract work in public relations. The problem with that quickly became evident when I started getting phone calls at all hours of the day and night from my clients. The expectation that I would be available for their needs 24/7 was too much, and I struggled to separate my personal time from work time. After a year I made the decision to put Jace into a nursery and looked into returning to the work place, but first I had to fix that gushing problem with my cycle.

About a year after that horrific incident at my old office, a mini birth control pill became available. The bills for the adoption were piling up and my depression was worsening. I felt that if I could just return to the work that I loved, get a bit of my old life back, the depression would go away. Plus, we really needed the money.

By some miracle, the mini pill did not upset my stomach, something that had plagued me with other birth control pills. I started pounding the pavement and eventually landed a good part-time job at the local government offices. Then, with the help of my new birth control pills, scheduled my periods to fall on my days off.

I was finally working, using my skills again. I got to dress up in suits and heels, wear make-up and do my hair. I was talking to other adults about important things, grown up things, not baby things! Each day I went to work excited to finally feel productive and accomplished. I know as a mother you are a production machine, but it is different from production in the professional world. I had missed work so much and loved being back in the thick of things.

I felt great, the bills for the adoption no longer seemed impossible, and Jace loved his new friends at the nursery. Life was looking up!

Well not everything was up. One really big thing was down. Way down.

My prolapse was worse than ever. Most days, my cervix would hang outside of my body. I could not be active in any form. Any movement or activity that put downward pressure on my pelvic floor hurt. Sitting on a bike seat or saddle hurt. Housecleaning hurt (oh who am I kidding, yes it hurt, but I wasn't heartbroken about this limitation). When I walked it felt like there was a bowling ball bouncing inside of me. If I walked for any length of time, that bowling ball would cause my whole abdominal and perineum areas to become painfully inflamed and irritated. Running was completely impossible. Lifting and carrying Jace hurt. He was a big baby and continued to grow quickly, even as a toddler. I tried to wear thongs under my dress slacks to prevent the dreaded VPL (visible panty line) but they rubbed and irritated my scar tissue so badly I quickly put them away again.

I had dealt with the complications around

my period and been able to return to work, but life was still a struggle. It was hard. I didn't want hard. I just wanted life to be easy again.

As much as I loved working, I started counting down the days until I could be done with work again. I worked for a year and a half, as we waded our way through the adoption process.

And then my second son came home.

Once again, life changed completely.

A Window Opens

The adoption process took well over two years and was a rollercoaster of a ride. Anyone who thinks adoption is the easy way to build a family is delusional.

It took almost a year to complete all the necessary criminal checks, medicals, and homestudies to create our dossier. It was during the building of our dossier that I returned to work to help pay for the bills that piled up. Once the dossier was shipped off to Ethiopia, we were promised we would have our baby home within a year.

They lied. It took over a year just to be matched with a gorgeous, doe-eyed little boy. He was ten weeks old, his name Yonas. That's when the truly painful and heart-wrenching part of the wait started. Changes in foreign policy caused delay after delay. We watched our baby growing up, without us, in an orphanage. Two months, four, six, eight. When Yonas was nine and half months old our adoption agency declared bankruptcy.

It was devastating. To be so far away from your child, knowing that he was suffering. We heard so many rumors. No food, caregivers leaving, our adoption being revoked. It was a terrifying time.

We raced. No that doesn't sound right; we didn't run, that damn bowling ball would have made it too painful even if I could have run half way around the world. We took planes, lots and lots of planes, over forty hours of travel, and finally landed in Addis Ababa, Ethiopia. Our son had been neglected, his body showing the signs of stress. A quick weigh-in told us he had lost a tenth of his body weight in a month.

We learned later that by the time we heard about the bankruptcy in Canada the orphanages had already been struggling without money for weeks.

Ethiopia was a beautiful, stunning, and heartbreaking country. I wish we could have visited under better circumstances. With less stress and more time. That trip had one goal, to get Yonas. Jace stayed in Canada, it was the first time we had been apart for more than twenty-four hours and all I wanted to do was get home and have my boys together under one roof. Safe and sound.

It was a crazy trip but we had him. Yonas was finally with us and, ten days after leaving Canada, we returned. Our family was complete now we had our two boys, ten month old Yonas and three year old Jace. We had reached the end goal. Everything from that point forward would work itself out. As long as we were together, we could overcome anything.

And we did.

But it took years of intense work.

People will try and tell you that it is better to experience trauma as an infant, 'because they won't remember anything'. The big flaw in this theory is that trauma, while the brain is developing so rapidly, actually causes far more damage, and more lifelong debilitating damage, compared to a mature brain exposed to trauma.

Yonas had been through intense, complex, long-term trauma. It was not something he was going to forget or from which he would spontaneously recover.

Yonas was ten months old when he came home. At the time, he fit perfectly into clothing for a nine month old. Not bad, right? Well in the first few months home he shot through all the sizes, finally slowing down once he was in clothing for three year olds at only fourteen months of age.

When a child is adopted, one of the most important activities is attachment parenting. The idea is to create a strong bond, closeness, and a high level of trust between child and parent, as quickly as possible. An adopted child believes, and knows, that parents can leave. This loss of anchoring for a child can negatively affect development and can cause many issues for the child and family unit. Therefore, it is critically important to instill in them a strong sense of belonging and place, so they can thrive in their new family and their new life.

I have always been a firm believer in attachment parenting, even with Jace. My parents did it with me and my sister, so I always considered it parenting. Just regular, old parenting.

Carrying, holding, and skin to skin contact are some of the most common attachment parenting techniques. I tried to employ all of these with Yonas but, due to my prolapses, my body struggled. The pain I experienced trying to carry Yonas around, was intense. I tried many types of carriers, something I had also used extensively with Jace, but Yonas was just so much bigger.

Yonas also had post-traumatic stress disorder and would experience terrifying panic attacks. It is amazing how much damage a thirty pound child can do to an adult when they are in an all-out fight or flight reaction. My body took the brunt of this damage. Shoulder and pelvic floor damage were the most common injuries I suffered while trying to keep him safe. As any mother can tell you, my body was expendable when it came to keeping my son safe. I knew what I was going through was damaging my body, but it didn't matter. What mattered was helping Yonas to heal, to feel safe.

Between Yonas's issues and my own health issues, we started staying home more and more. Going out in public was just not possible and usually ended up with at least one person in tears (who, me?). Around this time the depression started pressing in harder, heavier. It covered me like a dark cloud. It became hard to breathe. The world foggy. Moving was laborious. I had no motivation. I became angry, bitter. I prided myself on being a very patient, calm mother, but I started yelling and getting frustrated with the kids.

I tried. Boy, I tried so hard to be that amazing super-mom that everyone around me seemed to have mastered being so effortlessly. The first Christmas Yonas was home, when he was one and Jace was three years old, I decided my boys should learn about the spirit of Christmas, about giving back. We were going to donate toys to a local children's charity that provided impoverished families with gifts for their children on Christmas Day.

The day of our big delivery I was, as usual, in pain and feeling horrible, but I wanted to do it. I felt it was an important activity to earn some sort of elite mommy status. Who gifted this status I was not sure. Why it was so coveted, I really didn't know. But I felt an immense amount of pressure to achieve it.

My mommy brain was really distorting reality.

I had convinced myself that it was a critically important lesson for my boys to learn and they had to learn it at a young age.

As we drove, three year old Jace, my ever precocious son, asked, "Mom, are these boys and girls bad?"

"No sweetie, why?"

"Well if they were good, Santa would bring them toys so we wouldn't have to give them ours."

My stomach clenched in panic. I wriggled in my seat as I tried to figure out how to answer this question, and to relieve the sudden pressure on my bladder. I am not sure why, but panic and stress always make me need to pee!

As I wriggled, I approached a stop sign. I slowed down, not a car in sight. I rolled through the stop sign as I wriggled. Distracted.

Of course a cop was waiting in the bushes.

It was the most expensive lesson ever, between the ticket and my son figuring out that Santa doesn't really exist.

I officially sucked at being a super-mom. It seemed like I was always doing things wrong. I was always hurting. I just didn't want to hurt anymore. I was also suffering from depression as I grieved and learned to cope with Yonas's struggles. Having a special needs child brings its own grief and struggles for parents. Layering that on top of POP sent me into the darkest time of my life.

The next summer, about a year after Yonas came home, we decided to visit a friend for a playdate. I was in so much pain that day I could barely drive. In fact, the pain had been intensifying due to the constant strain being put on my pelvic floor caring for my boys and had reached an extreme level of chronic pain that was reminiscent of the first few months after my first son's birth.

Here I was, living with prolapse for over four years, and things were only getting worse. Unlike the pain right after delivery, which was localized to the torn perineum, it was now throughout my abdominal cavity, pelvic basket, and lower back. I had also started developing pelvic floor spasms. Picture a leg cramp, but instead it is all the muscles throughout your pelvic area and crotch locked in a spasm. Yes, it hurt that much, plus so much more. When it spasmed I would collapse to the ground, unable to move.

That day I wanted nothing more than to stay in my bed, a day spent in darkness and solitude. The last thing I wanted to do was leave the house.

Despite the excruciating levels of pain I was in, my boys were hyper and really needed to burn off some steam. They needed this playdate. It was my hope that I could sit and rest while the boys played. When we got to the house, our host had two large dogs. The dogs were friendly enough but my young son took one look at them and went into one of the worst fight or flight responses I have ever seen. I tried to kneel down and comfort him, but that wasn't enough, he wanted up, NOW. The problem was, when I tried to stand up holding him, my whole body collapsed. There was no way I could support his weight. My pelvic floor was trashed, barely supporting my body, let alone the added weight of my son.

My dear friend picked up my son and comforted him. Wiping away his tears as she cuddled him close, her hips swinging back and forth.

It broke my heart. I was so broken I couldn't even comfort my son.

I decided then and there that I would get the surgery. Even if it meant a hysterectomy. I needed to get healthy and strong again, for my boys. I couldn't live like this anymore.

I was going to get fixed. No matter the cost.

Or so I thought.

Ready For Surgery?

Once the decision had been made to meet with the surgeon, my whole outlook changed. No longer was I stuck in limbo, struggling through endless days of symptoms and pain. I finally had something to focus on that provided a light at the end of the tunnel. I had my all-important end goal, which meant I could start a new five year plan. I needed that five year plan, it gave me purpose and drive and, most of all, hope. I decided it would look like this - first year, complete surgery. Next four years, live free of prolapse and get my life back!

Okay, realistically, I live in Canada - two years to complete surgery - then live my life again!

I researched surgery options during the seven month wait for an appointment to see the prolapse specialist (like an intake nurse, who assesses patients for surgery suitability). The wait would have been longer but because I was already 'in the system' due to my previous evaluations, treatments and physical therapy they were able to 'fast track' my appointment.

I admit it, I rolled my eyes when the lady on the phone excitedly told me how this was great news and she could get me seen in under a year!

The plan was that this specialist would then refer me over to the surgeon, who I would meet a few months later. Seven months was a lot of time to fill reading about prolapse surgery. I learned about recovery times, surgical options, successes, failures. I dreamed of being free of pain. Of getting my old life back.

The internet is an amazing tool. I found so many options. It was my hope that I could have a seemingly simple suspension procedure, to lift everything up without the need to remove any organs. I reasoned with myself that it would be the most minimally invasive technique, and then, if or when it failed, hopefully I would be post-menopausal and I could look at a hysterectomy at that time. Although I wanted surgery, I still really wanted to keep my uterus. Something in my gut said it was important for my body.

My comfort level talking about POP was increasing and, now that I felt ready for the big step to surgery, I wanted to talk to my mother. Before that point I simply hadn't been comfortable talking about what was happening to my body. I was scared, ashamed, and so unsure. I found it much easier to stay silent, but facing surgery made me want to talk. And, once I was ready to talk, my mom was there, ready and waiting. Little had I known, but POP was all too familiar to my mother and grandmothers.

One day, while the boys watched cartoons and ate a huge bag of chips as if I never, ever fed them, my mother and I discussed pelvic organ prolapse extensively, while sipping tea. She told me her horror stories with POP, but also the successes my grandmothers had enjoyed. One of my grandmothers lived, surgery free, with POP her whole life, simply using a pessary to keep things comfortable. My other grandmother had a procedure they called a 'stitch-back', in England in the sixties. The procedure was simple enough; they took her stretched and over-extended ligaments, folded them back up onto themselves to shorten them and lift her uterus, then stitched the ligaments in the folded, shorter position. Her surgery lasted thirty-five years before she noticed anything starting to fall again. At that point she was eighty years old.

I discovered my mom's story was completely different, yet scarily familiar.

My mom and I are of similar build, similar height, and we are both redheads. I was her first born and her birth experience was a carbon copy of my birth experience with Jace. In both cases, forceps were used, resulting in tearing and prolapsing of the uterus, bladder and rectum. My mother's case was not as severe as mine, and she went on to successfully have one more baby, my younger sister. My sister's birth was without any significant trauma, but the existing damage was aggravated by the subsequent pregnancy causing a significant increase in her symptoms.

My mother wanted surgery to repair her prolapse and the surgeon at the time insisted on doing a hysterectomy, along with a repair to the vaginal canal. He said that leaving the ovaries ensured that she would go through menopause normally. Except she didn't. Almost immediately she went into early menopause, in her mid-thirties. She also developed severe scarring along the repair, which left her even more damaged than the original prolapse it was meant to repair. Over time she had many complications due to early menopause and the prolapse repair surgery. Complications that still plague her to this day.

I loved hearing the stories, even though I hated hearing how much my mother had suffered and continued to suffer. Like so many women with prolapse, it was something she had borne silently for many years. It felt good that we could finally talk about everything she had experienced.

My research had uncovered a number of medical studies that suggested one of the strongest indicators for prolapse risk was if your mother had prolapse.

I was batting a thousand, with my mother and both grandmothers having prolapse, and with my mother's story so similar to mine I was even more convinced that I wanted the modern version of the 'stitch-back' surgery my grandmother had received in England. I also became sure that my OBGYN should have asked about my medical history. She should have screened me and done a risk assessment for prolapse complications if I had a vaginal birth. Then, in light of the results, she should have discussed elective C-section with me due to my high risk factors.

I was facing surgery, likely multiple surgeries, no matter what. At least a C-section is only done once. At least I would have had my body and my life.

The one consistent thing I read from medical studies and personal stories, was that no POP surgery would last forever. The chance of requiring repeat surgeries was almost a certainty.

If I was lucky - really lucky - I might repeat my grandmother's success and live most of my life before prolapse came knocking again.

At that point I had been living with severe pelvic organ prolapse for over five years. I had spent so many hours trying to cope with the pain, discomfort and embarrassing side effects of POP, I was done with doing things naturally. I wanted to finally put it behind me and move on. I wanted surgery, but I wanted a good surgery that I could trust. I didn't want to deal with any of the horrors my mother, or other women online, had faced. Even if I had to get 'touch up' surgeries in ten or fifteen years, I was okay with that. I just wanted some relief and to get my life back.

My vision was that it would be like a face lift. Every few years I might need to go in for a touch up tuck and lift, but after the first major surgery the rest would be maintenance. Sadly, I have a very vivid imagination that does not usually line up with reality.

As I continued my research I became increasingly frustrated by the lack of information on POP. How could something be affecting the quality of life of millions of women, yet be almost completely ignored by society and the medical profession?

The pervasive thought on POP was that it is an extremely common 'old lady' problem, so, like a good little woman, I just needed to learn to live with it or get surgery. Or so I was repeatedly told.

I have never been a 'good little woman', just ask my husband.

In my situation, the pain continued to worsen as the years passed. There was none of this spontaneous healing, that I was promised by the OBGYN, within the first year postpartum. My two boys were extremely active and demanding of my time, not to mention, my physical and emotional energy too. A year after bringing Yonas home from Ethiopia he was diagnosed with Post Traumatic Stress Disorder (PTSD), Anxiety Disorder, Speech Delays, Sensory Processing Disorders, and some I don't even remember anymore. Parenting a special needs child is like parenting on steroids. You need to always be on, always be aware, always be intentional. There is no room for weakness on the part of the parents. And every single day I felt like a horrible mother if I did not run, play and have fun with my boys. Something as simple as picking up my two year old to comfort him after a scraped knee could leave me in pain that could last for days.

That bowling ball I talked about earlier? It was bigger, heavier. One day, while standing in front of the mirror after a shower, I noticed that my butt appeared to be getting really saggy. As I stared, in sadness and disgust at what my body had become, I realized it wasn't my butt, but the whole perineum bulging down. I pushed at it and realized it was bowing from the weight of my organs, pushing down from the inside. My organs were not on the outside because there was simply too much stuff trying to fit through that one tiny hole.

How's that for a visual? Sorry. I warned you: brutal honesty.

When I sat, especially on hard chairs or benches, I could feel those bulges, forcing me to always sit propped on one hip. I was deformed. Not just internally but now my deformity could be seen from the outside. The desire to curl up in bed and never leave washed over me like a tidal wave. My only life jacket - the promise of a miracle surgery that would fix everything.

Either live with it or get surgery, that was the mantra repeated over and over again. I wanted surgery. I wanted my body back. I was done. I was handing over my body on a silver platter with one request: please fix and return in one healthy, whole piece.

Then, finally, it was time. I met with the specialist who, upon realizing I had already tried physio and pessaries, fast tracked my appointment to meet with the surgeon. Less than four weeks later I was back at the hospital, ready to meet the surgeon.

And the Walls Came Tumbling Down

I went into the appointment armed with all the research I had done. I printed out reports, highlighting, with bright pink highlighter, the parts I thought related to my case. I had already decided exactly what I wanted, and I convinced myself that it was just a matter of being forceful and confident. They would have to listen and agree. I had a rock solid case.

There were two things I did not want as part of a surgery repair. The main one was a hysterectomy. I was in my mid-thirties and wanted to keep my womanly parts - they worked just fine; they just happened to be in the wrong place, after going for a wander while my son was being born. The second was using a mesh or foreign material to complete the repair. As I mentioned, I am extremely sensitive and reactive. That redhead thing - it's a pain in the ass, I'm telling you. If there was any chance of rejection (which, with mesh, was actually fairly high), I knew my body would reject. Mesh also had questionable success rates and rumors of class action lawsuits were starting to spring up. I conceded to myself that I could be convinced about the mesh with a really good argument, but the hysterectomy... no way. Not going there. Not after learning about the complications it caused for my mother.

Guess what the surgeon wanted to do? Yup, a hysterectomy and then use mesh to pull those tumbling walls back up. After that, she wanted to rebuild my vagina using mesh.

I did not, and still do not, see this type of surgery ending well for me.

In fact, the surgeon even went on to say that the chance of my body re-prolapsing was one hundred percent. So I would need at least one more surgery, probably more over my life span due to my young age, possibly as soon as six months post-op.

Due to my high risk of prolapsing again I would be limited to lifting no more than ten pounds for the rest of my life and would need to use extreme caution during any physical activities. Less than ten pounds would be safe, as long as I did not do it too much.

She also could not guarantee that my 'sexual functioning' would remain intact. She said she would do her best but women often found it too uncomfortable and painful after the surgery. I was in my mid-thirties and she was telling me that this surgery would leave me unable to have sex again for the rest of my life? Really?

But that wasn't all. As an afterthought, she added, "Oh, and the surgery will make you incontinent. That I can tell you for sure. Perhaps with some physio we can help with that, but I feel it is important to mention this to my patients."

Talk about a glowing endorsement!

Despite all my prolapse complications and issues, incontinence was thankfully something I rarely ever suffered from. I had frequency issues and would often do the potty dance, where I would go pee, stand up for a minute or two then sit back down and finish, but I did not leak uncontrollably. And I didn't want to start. Wearing a diaper in my thirties - and for the rest of my life - was not a side effect I was willing to accept.

Then again, if I was wearing a diaper maybe the sex part was not such a huge issue. I am pretty sure a diaper is not my, or Remy's, idea of sexy. Talk about a major mood killer.

Surgery was supposed to free me from

limitations, not make my life and activities more restrictive.

The surgeon also said I was a special and unique case, because of the severity of my damage and my age. Severe prolapses, scarring, plus extensive nerve and muscle damage was not something she had seen in many young people.

You never want to be special or unique when dealing with surgeons, it's not a good thing.

Now I tried to give her the benefit of the doubt. It was her profession, after all, but I was no longer naive about the damage a doctor could do to a body. My trust was not going to come easily and, frankly, her little speech did nothing to encourage my confidence in her.

My biggest issue was that what she proposed was major. There was no going back from the removal of organs and studies were showing that mesh complications were significant and very hard to correct if they occurred. I wanted to try a much more minimally invasive approach, like the stitch back to lift things up a bit and give me some relief. Make things down there a little easier to live with. Yes, it might have failed, but the surgeon said things were going to fail anyway, even if she went for the extreme option. Plus, what she was proposing would do nothing to help all the scarring, nerve and muscle damage. In fact, the surgeon said it would likely make those issues worse. Joy!

I argued and pleaded; why not do something now to make me comfortable, hopefully, for a few years, then when I hit menopause or whenever the walls come down again, then we could do something bigger, more extreme?

Nope, if I was going to have surgery, that was the only surgery she was willing to do.

I argued that my grandmother had a simple suspension surgery for her prolapse, that had lasted over thirty-five years before she prolapsed again.

Nope. The surgeon was firm. There was only one surgery she would do. A hysterectomy with mesh sling and rebuild.

I left the hospital so frustrated, depressed, and utterly defeated. I was so sick of being in pain. So tired of hurting.

Our medical system has its strengths, but it also has some glaring weaknesses. Getting a second opinion is a pain in the ass. This was the only surgeon in our area, so any second opinion would need to be done elsewhere in Canada, the USA, or even the world. The wait to get into see uro-gyn surgeons in Canada at the time was two to five years... yes, I said years. And that was just to get an evaluation. Surgery would be a year or two after the evaluation, if the surgeon agreed to do the procedure.

I looked into traveling to the United States, or even Europe, for surgery. The complications around traveling and undergoing surgery with two young boys made it seem like an insurmountable obstacle. Plus, how would I know if I had really found a good surgeon worth the trip? I was at a loss. I wanted surgery, but I wanted a surgery I felt confident would succeed, that I felt could give me my life back.

Yes, I am stubborn, but I had learned that no one was going to advocate for my best interests; it was up to me to be my biggest advocate. No one cared. It was up to me to care. Up to me to protect myself.

And I hated that feeling.

Depression and anger consumed me.

I hated how it was negatively affecting my life. I hated how it made me so inactive. I hated being in pain all the time. I hated not being able to be the mother I wanted to be. I hated how no one understood and that it was such a hard topic to discuss. I hated how it was making me into such a hater!

The surgery option was a very slippery slope. I needed to find balance, not become more unbalanced. I worried that if I let them start cutting I would tumble down the slope so fast I might never recover.

At that point, I knew my demon. After surgery, I had no idea what demonic nightmares could be waiting for me. I had read horror stories about mesh. I knew my mother's own battles with her health after having a hysterectomy and repair in her thirties without mesh. My gut was screaming at me that it was not right. That the surgeon was wrong.

There had to be something better. I just needed to find it.

The POP Heard Around the World

Adopting internationally meant opening my heart to a new culture, learning and adopting the heritage of my future child. I became involved in giving back, wanting to help where I saw so much struggle.

Supporting children's charities was an easy choice; I could see my future child in the eyes of every child on those glossy charity brochures and websites. My mothering instinct to protect them all kicked in quickly, with all the grace of a ferocious momma bear. I sponsored children, supported orphanages, and held fundraising events to pay school fees.

Slowly, another story started revealing itself. The story of these children's mothers, often no more than children themselves. Married as teenagers, or even worse, sometimes only children. Daughters were often seen as less important to invest in, so they would receive only the most basic schooling before being sent off to be married. Their bodies would still be growing, yet already they were carrying a new life.

In too many cases, their pregnancies ended in permanent disabilities or death.

In 2011, the United Nations Population Fund (UNFPA) released a report, *The State of World's Midwifery 2011: Delivering Health, Saving Lives*, that I read with my jaw hanging open. My mind flinched at the horrible truths being revealed, unable to believe, unable to comprehend and accept. The report stated that three point six million lives were lost every year - that is one thousand every single day - due to complications from pregnancy and childbirth that could have been prevented. In most cases due to inadequate or insufficient health care. The article explored the desperate need for more midwives to provide women and children, especially in developing countries, with appropriate medical care during their pregnancies and births to decrease these numbers.

Those numbers, those staggeringly unbelievable numbers, stopped me in my tracks.

In today's day and age, a thousand women and children were dying every day, and almost all of those deaths were preventable.

Like pelvic organ prolapse before I developed it, I wondered how did I not know this? How was this not front page news? Then another statistic in the article caught my attention, 99% of these losses were in developing countries, mainly sub-Saharan Africa.

I could not stop reading. The reality of our world was changing in front of my eyes.

One of the other causes that captured my heart in a vise-like grip, was women suffering from fistula.

When a child becomes stuck in the birth canal for an extended period of time (commonly called obstructed labor), the blood supply to the tissues is cut off. These tissues then start to die and the woman ends up with holes, through which urine and stool constantly leak. These women are ostracized by their communities, abandoned by their families, and forced to live an isolated existence.

Fistula has been almost completely eradicated in the developed world for years, since the advent of Cesarean sections. Yet, according to the Hamlin Fistula Hospital, two million women live with fistula with another one hundred thousand cases occurring every year.

I devoured books on women's health in

developing countries, my eyes and heart opening to the plight of my global sisters. Those two million women, their numbers growing, live with fistulas and face horrendous odds of getting treatment. The capacity to offer treatment hovered at only around sixty five hundred each year.

Getting medical care in these countries is extremely difficult and often excessively expensive based on regional income levels. There is very little information available about pelvic organ prolapse in places like Ethiopia, not because it doesn't exist, but because they do not have the medical services to meet the most basic of needs. A non-life threatening condition, such as prolapse, does not even warrant attention. These women suffer in silence with prolapse and so much more.

I honestly cannot imagine what life is like for these young women, often married and already having at least one baby before they are out of their teens.

One day I purchased a bracelet to help fund fistula surgeries in Ethiopia. As I sat in the surgeon's office, hearing all the bad news about my pelvic organ prolapse, and my lack of good surgery options, I gently rubbed the bracelet between my fingertips. During an extremely long period, when I was left alone in the office, I thought of the women of Ethiopia, suffering from fistulas. I imagined that perhaps, right at that moment, one young woman was lying awake, worried, scared and unsure in a hospital bed at the Fistula Hospital.

Just like me, but her needs so much more.

Despite my bad news, I was filled with hope for this young woman who, hopefully, would be given her life back by the amazing doctors at the Fistula Hospital. I whispered a blessing of sorts, my hope and wish for her simply that she will regain her dignity.

I believe I was saying the blessing as much for her as for me. Really that was all I wanted for myself too. That one day I could have my dignity back. My confidence back. My life back.

The issue of prolapse complications is a common thread that affects women around the world, regardless of age, race, lifestyle, location or wealth. The fact that fistula, one of the most severe results of traumatic childbirth, is such a prevalent concern in developing countries, only proves that 'lesser issues', such as prolapse, are likely widespread in the female population.

I was filled with horror that women lived like that, that they lived in shame. I hated that the women living like that are often not women at all, but girls. So young, so vulnerable. Children, forced to become women far too soon. Women in the developing world work so hard. Their lives are filled with long days of intense physical labor.

At the moment I needed it most, I was given some perspective on the extent of my blessings.

I read a lot about women's health issues in the developing world that night after meeting the surgeon. Perhaps to escape the reality of my own situation, but I like to think it was because I was finally in a place to let go, open my heart and embrace the knowledge.

It was sobering to learn that my delivery story would have ended very differently if, by an accident of birth, I had been born in the developing world. My birth story would have ended in either death for both myself and my son, or death for my son and a fistula for me.

The fog started to lift as I gained perspective. Suffering with severe pelvic organ prolapse and damage sucked. It really sucked. But what these women faced was so much worse. I started researching and supporting charities that aided women in the developing world. It gave me a sense of purpose, and I felt myself opening up, as I embraced the cause of women who struggled so much more than me.

The depression and grief were still there, but I started feeling stronger, more capable. I read so many stories of inspiration. Of women overcoming the most immense obstacles imaginable.

Walking days to reach a fistula hospital.

Living in a cramped shelter for years, until their bodies atrophied, yet one day walking again.

Surgeries that successfully repaired the most damaged of pelvic floors, allowing the women to not only return to their families, but to have more babies.

Of women undergoing surgery and therapy for over a year to restore bladder and bowel function, only to have it all fail, yet they turned around and started helping their sisters, in the hope that perhaps they could be healed.

These women never gave up. They fought. To me they were heroes. Warriors. Their stories helped me. They built me up. Lifted me up, until I felt I could do this. I could face prolapse head on, and not let it beat me. I wasn't sure how, or what I was going to do, but I felt there had to be a way for me to be strong. To have a full life again.

In fact, some of my first tentative steps in healing came from my research into therapy and treatments used to aid women recovering from fistula. Surgery was only part of their story; there were also months, sometimes years, of therapy. It was there that I started to learn how to care for my body.

Which, in so many ways, seems like the most unlikely of places. Who would have thought I would get my inspiration, and some of my knowledge, from third world hospitals? Yet here it was, people and hospitals dedicated to helping the most damaged of pelvic floors and bodies. Exactly what I needed.

They inspired me. They gave me hope. They gave me a purpose.

For the first time I thought I might ready to tackle my health head on. To be strong, to be a warrior in the battle to save my own health.

In the light of day I could build myself up, but at night that dark cloud of depression still weighed heavily. The doubts and fears taking hold when I least expected them. Like a snake in the grass, ready to strike without warning.

Parenting In Pain

As I was exploring the surgery route, it was becoming harder and harder for me to keep up with my boys. They were getting bigger, stronger. Playing harder and longer. They loved to play together, but what they loved more was having Mommy play with them. My boys did not understand what was wrong with me. They did not realize how much they physically hurt me, how their actions, rough play, and special needs caused me so much pain.

I also believed it was wrong of me to put that weight on them. They were too young. I needed to tough it out. I needed to be a super-mom.

At this age they were too young to understand that Mommy was broken in her girly parts, and it was the kind of broken that does not get better in a few minutes, like one of their boo-boos. It was the kind of broken that hurt when I picked them up or tried to play their games. A hurt that never went away, only the intensity varying slightly day by day, hour by hour.

I would try to ride my boys' ride-on cars... these cool little kinetic powered skateboard shaped things with handle bars that you pumped back and forth to go faster and faster. The boys loved to race around on these things for hours. They set up obstacle courses, they raced head to head, spinning around and around our basement. They begged me to join in the fun, to race with them. I tried once, for one round of racing and, oh, the pain in my behind!

Jumping, running, trampolining, skipping - were all out of the question. That bowling ball could literally take the wind from my lungs with one good bounce. Not to mention those bounces often lead to leaking.

Going anywhere that left me without a washroom for more than thirty minutes was something that turned me into a nervous wreck. If I had to do it, I would avoid drinking anything for at least four hours before the outing in an attempt to control the bladder issues. I also became reliant on my husband and parents to accompany me on outings. Constantly taking the boys with me into the washroom was a major challenge. For some reason, leaving fun festivals and games to go with Mom to the washroom was not their idea of fun. Go figure.

Having extra adult supervision allowed me to duck off to the washroom at a moment's notice. This made outings, that would have been impossible solo, possible. I am not sure how I would have made it through that time without their support.

Yet, relying on that support also added to my feelings of failure. Our society values independence.

On one occasion, I was at a community gathering talking to some other mothers. My kids were pulling me in multiple directions and I made a hollow joke, "Boy, it's impossible keeping up with these two!"

More than one mother in the group scoffed, a more vocal one said, "Try three, four, or five kids!" I looked up at the many nodding heads around me and felt like shrinking to the size of a gnat.

I know it would be harder with more hyperactive bodies to chase and care for, that's why we stopped at two! But that doesn't mean what I am facing is easy or less of a challenge.

I am not sure why so many parents feel the

need to one up each other. Parenting is hard. For all of us. I believe there is an opportunity to compare our struggles and support one another in our battles, without belittling or diminishing the challenges we face. Depression does not come with a neon sign. Many special needs kids save their most destructive and extreme behaviors for when they are safely in their homes, where only the closest of family can witness their loss of control and pain.

I rarely spoke about my own turmoil, or the struggles my children faced. When I did, it was always off the cuff to test the waters. More often than not, I was dismissed or ridiculed, not intentionally, but from a place of ignorance. That didn't mean it hurt any less.

So I withdrew even more. I found it harder and harder to relate to other mothers. To make the proper small talk, that would include me in their exclusive cliques when all I could think about was what might set off my son's PTSD, or if he was being socially appropriate, or worrying about what my body might do. Leaking urine or blood, and explosive fanny farts, are not things most people look for in new friends.

I created this burden myself. A part of me knew this, my flair for the dramatic was at times mighty, but I didn't know how to unburden myself. Pain and depression were in control.

I knew I was the worst kind of failure as a mother when I would tell my boys: "I can't play... again. No, I don't think I will be able to play later."

It seemed so unfair, watching parents with healthy bodies wrestling and tossing their kids around, or carrying their toddlers with ease. Or planning these long, fun-filled days of family activities, that I knew would leave me broken down in pain for a week if I tried the same thing with my family.

A long car ride sitting on that bulge? No, thank you.

I was so jealous of those parents and their pain free bodies. They did not understand. If I tried to explain their eyes would glaze over or they would make ludicrous suggestions for how to suddenly feel better. As if I hadn't already tried everything over the previous five years.

One of the things I tried was an inversion table. We had bought it, years earlier, for my husband who had suffered from a damaged spine due to a car accident. I reasoned that if gravity was my enemy, then flipping upside-down would make gravity my friend.

It relieved the pressure. I could feel all my organs and tissues sliding up! It also made me dizzy and light-headed. Then, as soon as I flipped back onto my feet, everything slipped down again, usually with a painful thud as it hit my perineum.

My biggest challenge was trying to address all the urgent needs of my toddler and preschooler, 'I need the potty', 'I'm thirsty', 'I hurt my toe', with the needs of my body. Although I was not usually incontinent, when I had to go, I *had* to go, right that second. Often I would make it to the bathroom but not onto the toilet in time, after being distracted by the children on the way.

I also struggled with having the time and privacy for bowel movements. One of the biggest lessons I learned was to never strain; but often I would be sitting, trying to do my business, and I would hear crashing, crying, demands for something or another. Staying relaxed was futile.

Remember the issue with gushing? How do I explain to my children that we need to stop playing and go inside because Mom needs to go to the bathroom *now*? Or when the children burst into the washroom and then freak out at the sight of all the blood?

Parenting such young children with a severe case of prolapse was so hard. It seemed never ending. Each day an impossible challenge. A challenge I was sure I failed, over and over again.

Sometimes I just wanted to be left alone, to deal with the constant demands and needs of my body without trying to balance the needs of two young children. This was especially true of my youngest, who required direct, line of sight, care for over two years. That meant I had to take him everywhere with me. Those washroom visits? The door had to be kept open at all times. I had to always have eyes on him, unless he was sleeping. How was I ever going to find balance in my own body when I had so many things constantly pulling at me?

The depression convinced me it was an impossible task. Pulling me deeper and deeper into its grasp.

Social Struggles

At one point a close friend and fellow mother had her babies very close together, both delivered by C-section, then months later bought herself a motorcycle. I sat on that motorcycle once, trying to be the supportive friend, saying how cool and amazing it was that she had a bike. The truth was, it hurt. Sitting on a motorcycle hurt so much down there. It also hurt my heart. I was sad. I was mad.

Why did she get a C-section, which allowed her to keep her body and enjoy such a carefree motherhood, while I was cursed with so much pain and suffering? Why didn't my doctor do the ultrasounds I asked for? Why didn't my doctor ask me to collect a family history about these issues? Why didn't my doctor ask the questions I didn't know to ask that would have shown I was an extremely high risk for prolapse? Why didn't my doctor screen me for prolapse risk factors? Why didn't my doctor do a damn C-section which would have given me the motherhood life that my friend so casually enjoyed?

I didn't want to feel this way. I hated myself, beat myself up, told myself to get over it. Toughen up already. I tried to fake it. 'Fake it 'til you make it' was a mantra commonly used in the adoption world as a way to cope during the difficult first year after a child joins a family. I tried to apply it to my situation, pretending and faking, as if nothing was wrong. I was happy, happy, happy!

It felt wrong, false. Like wearing a mask that didn't fit quite right and obscured my vision.

Friends would often ask me to go on special outings and playdates with the kids. Yonas's PTSD caused him to be terrified of strangers and new situations. As part of the PTSD he would have 'fight or flight' reactions that could be extremely violent.

One day we decided to visit a local dinosaur attraction that was a favorite of the boys. I loved it because Yonas felt safe there and the boys were so obsessed with dinosaurs that they always had a great time during our visits. It was mid-

August and hot, a perfect day to visit the dinosaurs. Yonas was three years old, but had continued to defy conventional growth charts and was the size of an average 6 year old, or roughly the size of his brother, Jace.

Two minutes past the gates something happened. I still don't know what it was but something triggered a PTSD attack. Yonas took off running, his voice a high pitched wail of fright, as his arms punched at the air. The grounds were busy with happy, chaotic families and, within a breath, Yonas was gone from my sight.

My chest felt like it was trapped in a painful vise. When Yonas had these attacks he had absolutely no sense of self-protection or self-preservation. He would run in front of cars without blinking or submerge himself in water without trying to surface. It was as if his mind entered a completely different zone. I knew we were in serious trouble.

I grabbed Jace around his middle, hoisting him like a football under my arm as I started running. Jace weighed about forty five pounds, and with every frantic step my heart pounded painfully in my chest and my cervix pushed its way farther and farther out of my body. I could feel my pelvic floor stretching under the pressure.

But it didn't matter. My body did not

matter. What mattered was getting to Yonas. I needed him safe. We ran for over five minutes until I finally spotted him, jumping and twitching, as he ran behind a building. I raced around the back of the building just in time to see Yonas stumble to the ground.

I set Jace down. “Wait here. Don’t move.” His eyes were wide with fear and anxiety. In retrospect, it was not surprising that within two years of living with Yonas’s PTSD attacks, Jace developed his own anxiety disorder. When your brother is terrified of the world, it makes a child start to wonder if there really are things out there to warrant the terror he saw in his brother.

I staggered up to Yonas, falling to my knees beside him. He was shaking, crying, his eyes unfocused and wide with fright. I tried to touch him but he cringed away. He often didn’t want to be touched when he was in the midst of an attack. A moment later I had no choice, as he tried to stand and take off again. I wrapped my arms around him. He weighed forty two pounds but in that state it felt more like one hundred pounds. He struggled and fought against me but I held tight, my arms locked around him in a bear hug as I hummed a soothing melody in his ear. After a few minutes he started to relax as his breathing regulated and his pupils contracted, allowing his eyes to focus again.

When triggered like he was that day, it would

take up to two days for him to regulate again. During that time he would be prone to diarrhea, vomiting, nightmares and hyperactivity. He would need constant, close support until he was fully calm again. The hours and days following an episode involved lots of carrying and holding to help reassure him.

After an episode, Yonas often adopted a coping mechanism where he would drop to the ground in a heap, as if playing dead. As I held his hand on the way out of the dinosaur park, he did exactly that, dropping to the ground suddenly and without warning. He hurt my shoulder, neck and back. Not to mention added damage to my already suffering pelvic floor. He stayed on the ground, unmoving. Even his breaths became shallow. There was no choice, I had to carry him to the car. I don't know how I did it, but I did. At least that day I only had to carry him. Some days Jace would hit the wall, his own terrors triggered by his brother's, and I would find myself carrying both boys.

Our biggest struggle was that we could not predict what would cause a PTSD episode. It could be triggered by an insect, a woman's perfume, a voice, or something none of us could even detect. I never knew when it was going to happen until he had an attack. I was always on edge, always ready. When it would happen, I would have to act quickly. I could never relax and 'just let the kids play'.

Between Yonas and I, and our various issues, outings were too hard, too stressful, and definitely not fun.

I felt like I was constantly hurting. I just didn't want to hurt anymore. When I was hurting it became impossible to parent intentionally, compassionately, following attachment parenting techniques. My youngest son especially, but both my boys, needed me as whole and healthy as I could be. So we stopped going out.

We turned down the fancy outings, the trips to the lake, the parties. Instead we stayed home, where I had better control over my environment and could do things to protect my body and keep my children happy.

I was constantly disappointed in myself when I needed to take the easy way out, by allowing my kids to have that popsicle, or extra time on the computer game, because the alternative involved them asking me, yet again, to do something I could not do, due to pain.

During this time, after learning that surgery was not going to be the miracle cure I had hoped, depression weighed heavily on me. I felt like such a failure. I felt like I was a complete failure as a mother. In becoming a mother, I had lost everything. I had lost myself, and I didn't know how to find my way out. The thing

I had hung my flag on for so many years, the miraculous surgery that was going to cure everything, was no longer there. It was as if someone had turned off the light, leaving me stranded with nothing to guide me.

I could not relate to other mothers. They did not understand why I was struggling so much. I felt judged and ridiculed.

One time, a friend went on a rant about how she envied my status as a stay-at-home mom and how I was the luckiest person she knew. It was a bad day. I was fed up. How could all these people, who claimed to be my friends, not get what I was going through? I regret I went on my own rant that day.

"Really? Would you like to have your organs falling out of your body? Living in shame and fear because of something you didn't ask for, and can't be fixed? Being forced to hide in your home because of pain and embarrassing complications such as bleeding all over a chair in a meeting? I'm not living the high life, eating bonbons and playing with the kids all day while Remy is away at work. My situation is not enviable at all. This was not a choice."

Some days you hit a wall. That day I hit hard. My friend never did get it. Instead, she felt attacked or like I was way over reacting.

It seemed there was just no way to be heard.

POP is so huge. So all-encompassing in a

woman's life. It can be impossible for someone to comprehend the impact if they have not lived with it. That day, sadly in anger, I tried to educate someone. It backfired. Some days you really cannot win.

When people would go on and on about how lucky I was to stay home with my boys, I got angry. I didn't blow up like I did that one time, but it resulted in that internal, seething anger that eats away at you.

How could they not see this was not a lifestyle choice, that I had loved my career and it was not something I had willingly given up? Being a stay-at-home mom was not a choice, it was a confinement, a jail sentence, forced on me by POP. I could no longer relate to the people I had once called friends. They just did not get it and could not see the reality of my days.

I started building walls, shielding myself from the pain. Depression pressed in harder.

I know it sounds dramatic, and I have been known to have a flair for drama, but these kinds of things hurt. Parenting is a thankless job. I found myself on the end of so much judgment and lack of understanding or caring. No one wanted to hear about my broken lady parts, or how much I was struggling with pain, as I tried to parent my boys. But I was also not sure it was something I wanted to share anyway. I was ashamed. Ashamed of my failures.

The loneliness settled over me, layering on top of the grief, anger and depression.

Thank goodness I had discovered the stories of women in the developing world. Reading those stories gave me perspective and hope. It made me feel stronger and able to do what I needed to do to get through.

I started to focus only on what was important: myself and my family. I hardened my shell to the judgments and comments. I convinced myself not to worry about what other people thought or how they judged me. My kids needed me. They needed me as whole and healthy as I could be. I needed to find a new way. A few months after meeting with the surgeon, I once again turned to the internet; but this time, instead of visiting medical research sites, I visited some forums and social groups. And for the first time, I felt that, maybe, I wasn't alone.

PART 4

TAKING BACK MY LIFE

Taking Control

Taking control of my body and my health was scary. I wasn't sure where to start, and for every bit of information I found there was so much controversy. Some people would swear by one treatment course, others would pan it as voodoo, yet others would claim it could cause more harm. There was no one putting any real research into natural ways of coping with pelvic organ prolapse. Medical professionals, doctors, therapists, all chanted the same word over and over again, kegel, Kegel, KEGEL!

I tried to Kegel. Oh, I squeezed and squeezed, but those muscles down there would not do anything. Not even a twitch. My muscle damage was too severe. I thought maybe I was doing Kegels wrong.

During more than one extremely embarrassing examination, I would find myself naked, my legs up in the air, a stranger's fingers inside my vagina as they told me repeatedly to squeeze. I would squeeze so hard I would see stars, but nothing down there would move.

"Bear down like you want to pass gas."

Grunt, strain. Nothing.

"Don't use your abdominals, just pretend you are trying to stop the passing of urine or gas."

Grunt, strain, grit my teeth. Nothing.

"Sorry, nothing is happening. You should keep trying. Oh, you have been trying for five years? Well, keep at it."

Did they have any advice on how to do them right? A lesson to teach me? A training schedule?

Well no, they would wave their hands and say something very unhelpful like, "Try and stop the flow of urine." I could do that, honestly I could. Of all the issues I faced, thankfully, leaking was not one of them. Well okay, not all the time. I mean, when things were urgent there was no stopping the flow, but most of the time I could stop mid-flow. But that did not mean any of the other muscles down there were working.

I was in my mid-thirties and madly in love with my husband. Sex was not as frequent as we would have liked, having young children definitely puts a crimp in the closed door activities, but we were still squeezing it in whenever we could.

Squeezing being a key word here. Nothing down there would squeeze or do anything during sex. The rest of my body was happy, happy, happy, but inside nothing moved, nothing reacted. I missed the feeling I enjoyed before kids, when my insides would clench, my insides fully participating in the act.

After trying every medical professional I could find, I gave up. It was time to start doing things myself.

One day I was in the kitchen, taken to my knees by an extremely painful pelvic floor spasm. My hands were shaking as I pressed them into the floor, trying not to lose my balance as I struggled to stand, but finding myself stuck, hunched over, unable to straighten my spine. Twisted up like a plastic bag caught in the wind. I staggered to the washroom, limping, fighting tears. I wanted to jump in the car that minute, go straight back to the surgeon and let her do whatever she wanted. I just wanted this over. As I sat on the toilet, trying to get my pelvic floor to relax, Remy came home.

My beloved husband can be annoyingly logical and practical. Something my over wrought dramatic self finds very frustrating, but the more sane part of me loves, because it keeps that drama queen under control.

We talked, and talked, and talked. He asked me if I really wanted surgery.

I said, "No, well at least not until after menopause. Especially if they are going to insist on taking my uterus."

"So, when is that?" he asked, his voice even, soothing.

"I dunno, maybe fifty?" I pouted, my drama queen fighting his practicality.

"So we need to find something you can do that will make this livable for the next fifteen years."

"Like what? Women either get a pessary, which I can't do, or surgery, which I don't want to do," I whined. My drama queen self liked to whine and bemoan.

"Sweetie, you are one of the best researchers I have ever met. Treat this like a research project. Find other options, evaluate them, then start trying some of the things you discover. If anything can increase your comfort by even a small amount, that is a good thing."

"But what if it's really expensive?"

"We will find the money. Your health is worth it. You are worth it. You are the best investment of our money. So don't worry about the money. Just give it a try. I want you healthy again." Then he pulled me into a big bear hug. My drama queen fled the building.

With a deep breath I turned around, walked to my computer and started researching.

My mission accepted. It was time for some action. Even if I failed, I needed to at least try.

Finding a New Way

It was daunting. And overwhelming. And confusing. There was so much information. So many different opinions, but very little real research. I spent a lot of time reading medical journals and forums.

I started my own journal, recording notes and ideas. Soon it was overflowing. After a month of research, I decided it was time to start implementing some of the techniques.

The first step was easy. I had read some articles that suggested Vitamin D and Fish Oils are beneficial for women struggling with prolapse. These same two supplements were highly recommended by our pediatrician for our children. A quick trip to our health store and I had what I needed to start the family on regular supplements. Since bowel movements were often a struggle, due to my misplaced anus and all (biscuits, anyone?), I also added magnesium to my supplements.

Now, I did not see a big change from the Vitamin D and Fish Oil, but those innocent looking magnesium pills were amazing.

I shouldn't say I saw no change from the Vitamin D and Fish Oils. The impact was just much more subtle. I do believe they were helping strengthen my body in ways that made other healing techniques I tried later on, more effective.

Not everything created an obvious change. Some things were small, little baby steps, but when added together brought about big improvements.

Even though I had a healthy diet, high in fibre, I struggled with constipation. One, and only one, magnesium daily kept things moving easily. One day I decided to try two. I spent the next morning sitting on the toilet! After that I kept it to just one magnesium. And the best part? It felt like things shifted down there, suddenly the hole seemed to be back where it should be. I cheered; I had my first little success!

Emboldened by the success of magnesium, I decided it was time to start tackling fitness. I had always been a very fit person. There is something about the way you feel when your body is strong and healthy, it strengthens your mind as well. I missed feeling strong and physically capable. In the years since my pregnancy and prolapse development, I had gained over fifteen pounds and lost all my muscle. Pre-babies I had sported a six pack, now I had nothing but rolls. I hated that feeling.

I found some short videos on the internet featuring exercises for women with prolapse. I started doing those videos but quickly needed something more. I found a physiotherapist that specialized in the pelvic floor. She had created a fitness DVD that a number of women raved about. I ordered it and waited anxiously for it to arrive.

As I ripped open the parcel I could not wait to get started. I cleared a space and started the video. The intro said I needed a large exercise ball and a smaller rubber ball. I ran off to the kids' play room and came back with the two balls. By now Yonas and Jace were very curious. My boys loved playing ball, but balls were not allowed in the living room. When they saw me bringing the balls up they dropped everything to come and see what I was doing.

I should have known I was starting something.

Two minutes into the video, as I was perching myself delicately on the edge of the large ball, butt out, sitting up straight, I was tackled. With cries of glee my boys thought this looked like the greatest game ever.

I tried to sit the boys down in front of some toys, but nope, the draw of the balls was too much.

Knowing there was no way I was going to be able to safely work out around my boisterous children I decided the least I could do was watch the video. In the end I sat on the ball, alternately giving each boy a 'bouncy ride' while I tried to watch the video over their heads.

From that day forward I was able to do the workouts three days a week when Jace was in school and Yonas was napping. At first this stressed me out; I wanted to do the workouts every day. I was committed. I knew the fastest way to results was to work every single day but, like any mother of little ones, I had to find a balance. That meant only being able to do the videos three times a week.

Within a few weeks, I had started to memorize a lot of the programs and exercises. Bit by bit, I realized I could incorporate the exercises into my regular daily activities. As the boys would run and play, I would step to the side and do a few squats or stretches. I couldn't fit in a thirty minute workout session, but I was able to do a few exercises here, then a few more minutes there, and at the end of the day I was happy to see that I was making fitness a part of my whole day.

One of the things I learned was how to do proper Kegels. For years everyone had talked on and on about squeezing as if trying to stop urine or gas, but they were missing a lot of really important parts of the Kegel. I learned one of the most important parts of the Kegel was being able to fully relax the muscles down there.

I had this light bulb moment when one article compared the pelvic floor to the arm muscles. If you only worked the bicep you would end up with a huge, bulging muscle on the top of your arm, but everything else about your arm would be weak and your arm would end up permanently contracted, bent at the elbow from the tight bicep, making your arm essentially useless. The pelvic floor was the same. It was not a matter of tightening the muscles constantly around my bladder, vagina and rectum, it was about working all the muscles in the pelvic floor basket so the strength was balanced, the pelvic floor strong but flexible.

I started learning how to isolate muscles throughout my abdomen and core, I learned about posture, and most of all I learned that I needed to start working my butt. Busting my butt with squats gave me one of my first fitness breakthroughs. I realized not only did I have muscle damage, but the muscles that were still functioning, were constantly tight and contracted. There was simply no more room to get any tighter, adding to the impossibility of doing Kegels. Due to the pressure from my falling organs, I was constantly flexing the muscles down there as I tried to hold things inside, and now I had a hypertonic pelvic floor.

In fact, I'd likely had a hypertonic pelvic floor most of my life. I grew up riding horses and being told to tuck in my bum. Tucking in your bum creates a hypertonic pelvic floor. When I joined fitness clubs, the instructors told me to tuck in my bum. Everywhere I went, people had been telling me to tuck in my bum since I was a small child in dance class and riding ponies.

When I finally untucked my bum, and stuck out my booty into some of the carefully designed squats, it felt like I had opened a dam. Everything suddenly relaxed as my whole body let go. It felt AMAZING!

One of my symptoms, that I did not realize was a symptom of my prolapse, was tailbone pain. It had started hurting during my pregnancy as a dull ache. Something easy to dismiss as 'another pregnancy pain'. After delivery the pain intensified and never did go away. If I sat for any length of time it hurt even more. I heard stories of tailbones being damaged, dislocated and even broken during deliveries, so I always assumed something had happened during the birth that damaged my tailbone.

Turns out it was the tension and pulling on my tailbone from my hypertonic pelvic floor that was causing all my grief. Once I got the right muscles working, and most importantly the right muscles relaxing, that tailbone pain went away. Years later my tailbone rarely ever hurts, but the second I feel any pain I do a few squats and other exercises to relax my pelvic floor and the pain disappears again.

Early on, when I first started doing the squats, I had to do them in the shower. Remember how I said I didn't leak? Well, when I finally let go and allowed my pelvic floor to relax I found I did leak a bit. So part of my morning shower routine, after soap, shampoo and conditioner, was some deep squats while allowing my bladder to empty.

I have never enjoyed peeing in the shower so much!

I was exercising safely, in a way that did not make my cervix pop out of my body, and made my whole body feel better. It was another big success moment.

I felt the blanket of depression slipping. Rays of hope were sneaking in.

Positive things were happening but I was still

hanging low. I needed to find a way to lift things, to tuck my organs up a little higher and relieve the pressure on my perineum. And I needed something to help strengthen those muscles that were not working properly, while relaxing those that were tight.

The pain was also still there. It was changing but not going away. All of this meant I had made progress, but still had a long way to go if I was going to make this viable until menopause.

In my research I had turned up some options. I had an idea how this could be done, but I was nervous. The technique scared me.

Zibber Zabber

I am a book lover, so one of my research stops was the local library. A search for pelvic organ prolapse turned up zero matches. ZERO! Half of all women will suffer from pelvic organ prolapse and my library didn't carry even one book on the topic? It was infuriating, and even more evidence that POP was an invisible disability that no one wanted to talk about or acknowledge.

I knew the information was out there, and I can be very determined when I sink my teeth into something. In this case I felt like a rabid dog; I was not going to give up on my goal to avoid and delay surgery easily. I knew there had to be more out there. I just needed to find it.

And if no one was talking, I would find the people who were talking.

Along the way there were some small successes but not all my experiments went well. While trying to learn about posture and alignment I discovered an array of conflicting advice. No strong, true analytical research, but a lot of anecdotal references and statements.

I picked one resource and decided to follow their guidance on posture and alignment. I lasted two hours. The technique had me walking around like a duck with my butt stuck out so far it left me with a sore back for days.

I know at times Remy was convinced I was losing it, but that day he was sure I was going quackers! (Sorry, couldn't resist the bad pun.)

In my quest to get my cervix to stay a little higher I met with the pessary specialist again. This time she found a pessary, a blue donut one, that kind of fit. At least it wasn't painful; I was able to stand up straight, and a after a few hops and bounces in the examination room, it seemed to stay in place. I was not truly sold on it, but hoped it would give me some relief and support at least some of the time.

I wore it home and could feel the pressure on my bladder as I drove. Not good. I had to go and pick up the boys. Within thirty minutes of standing, walking, bending and squatting as I cared for the boys it had slipped down to just inside the vaginal opening. There it irritated my scars and stretched my perineum until the whole area became painfully inflamed.

The next morning I called the pessary nurse. She said the problem was that I had too much nerve damage, extensive structural damage to my vagina and too much weight from all my prolapsing tissues. Perhaps I should meet with the surgeon?

I turned down her offer politely, through clenched teeth, then hung up.

The pessary has been collecting dust in my drawer for years and I haven't called the clinic since that day.

The setbacks were tough. Frustrating. When they weren't insanely funny.

Of all the things I have tried over the years, the one that takes the crown for causing the most absurdity and giggles, is a little thing I affectionately call my Zibber Zabber. Note this is not the proper brand name, just in case you were about to go searching!

In my early twenties I visited a physiotherapist to help with a jaw disorder. I went one time only. The therapist sat me in the middle of a crowded room. There were no curtains to separate patients, definitely no walls. Everyone was on display for everyone else to watch. The therapist stuck electrodes to my face, like a series of bizarre robot bandaids, complete with wires, then he cranked it up.

My face started twitching and jerking like I had jumping beans embedded in my skin. Then he left. Unable to talk or make eye contact (my eyeballs were bouncing and wiggling in time with the electrode zaps), I tried to hide my twitchy self from the crowds of people around me. It was horrible, but not painful. Perhaps, given time, the eStim would have helped my jaw disorder (known as TMJ disorder), but I was far too embarrassed to go back.

Although it was only one brief experience, the theory of eStim was not new to me when it came up during my research on POP treatments.

It took me a long time to build up the nerve to even consider ordering my Zibber Zabber. I mean really, I knew what eStim did to my face. Did I really want my vagina twitching like an alley cat?

The light bulb went off one day as I was doing exercises and Kegels. It occurred to me that the truth of the matter was that twitching was exactly what I was trying to achieve every time I tried to do Kegels. The lack of muscle engagement down there was so frustrating. I wanted to be able to use those muscles again.

Desperate times people, desperate times. I still wanted to avoid that extreme surgery and in the words of my wise husband, "If it buys you even a small amount of improvement, it's worth it."

He also does the dishes and laundry. He's a keeper!

So, with Remy's encouragement, I took the leap and ordered my Zibber Zabber. Turns out the systems were not available in Canada, so I ordered one from the United Kingdom.

It arrived in a very plain blue wrapper. Very discreet. Which I appreciated. I am not sure I wanted my mailman knowing I was zapping my privates. Some things just do not need to be shared with strangers, especially strangers I see every day!

The official terminology for what I purchased was an Electronic Stimulation Pelvic Exerciser. It arrived with a control unit and an assortment of probes that hooked into it.

Oh, and the manual. You would think any gizmo that is being used to zap your privates would come with a HUGE manual. Nope, it was this teeny tiny thing, about two inches by three inches, maybe 20 pages long, and decorated in pleasant whites and pinks. It wasn't a manual, more of a booklet.

I've had vibrators with more extensive instructions!

That night I had a bubble bath, then stretched out in bed, the lights dimmed. It sounds all romantic and stuff, but I was just trying to find a way to calm myself. I was so nervous!

With a shaking hand I lubricated the probe before sliding it inside. Tentatively, I pressed the 'on' button. The digital screen lit up, offering me a choice in programs and strengths. Squirming my way to the edge of the bed I reached onto the bedside table for the booklet-manual which outlined the various program options. Flipping the pages I found one designed for prolapse and pressed buttons until the control unit showed the correct program. Then, bit by bit, I increased the intensity and strength. The manual recommended a setting of thirty milli-amps. I pressed the up button until the screen showed 30.

Nothing happened.

The Moment of Change

Well, not nothing. I thought I might have felt a slight tingling, if I closed my eyes and concentrated really hard.

Now, the next thing I did will go down as one of my less than stellar moments.

I wanted to make sure it was working. The screen was coming on but maybe the probe or one of the wires that connected the probe to the base unit wasn't working. I needed to test it.

Seemed reasonable enough at the time.

I turned the probe off and took it out. Then, holding it clutched in my fist, I turned it back on and pressed the 'up' button that controlled the intensity.

I felt the tingling sensation right away.

Keeping my finger pressed down to increase the intensity, I waited. Within less than five seconds the unit had reached ten milli-amps and my arm convulsed, snapping back on itself, whacking me upside the head. The really stupid part was that I dropped the controller but couldn't get my other hand to release the probe. It remained in a twitching, painful, white knuckled fist.

With a shriek of panic and desperation I rolled onto my side, managed to grab the controller and turned it off, my arm and hand instantly relaxed.

I had my answer. It worked.

I never again touched the probe to any other part of my body. It may take me a while to learn some lessons, but that one etched itself onto my brain vividly and instantly.

Once I caught my breath, and my heart rate returned to normal, I inserted the probe again and turned it on. This time I watched in wonder as the numbers steadily climbed, my vagina barely registering anything until I hit fifty milli-amps. I could feel things twitching a bit. I decided to keep going. At sixty I stopped.

My muscles were pulsing, contracting with each round of electrical stimulation. For the first time in almost six years, my vaginal muscles were moving!

It felt amazing, like a deep massage for my vagina.

The program lasted twenty minutes.

The next day I ached down there. A good ache, the kind you get after a successful, sweaty, intense workout. I did it again the next night. Briefly. I experimented by turning the probe to see if I could engage the muscles better. A painful current shot down through my hip into my leg. I had found one of those damaged nerves. A few tentative adjustments revealed even more damaged nerves. So I kept the probe firmly placed, away from the nerves and let it Zibber Zabber away.

While chatting with some people online I was told that many people wear their Zibber Zabber while sitting up or even walking around making coffee and doing light work.

This sounded like a great idea. I could Zibber Zabber while taking care of my little ones!

One problem, the second I sat up the probe slipped a bit. By the time I was standing the probe had slipped to the opening causing me to jump and twitch as my perineum went crazy. Lying down I quickly turned it off and repositioned it before starting it again. Over time I have tried many times to use my Zibber Zabber in a position other than lying down, but my prolapses push down too heavily and the muscle and nerve damage are too severe. At times even lying down was not enough, I needed to prop my hips up on a pillow so my organs would slide up out of the way. Honestly, I didn't see it as a major loss. I was always on the go and being forced to stretch out and relax for twenty minutes at the end of the day - pure bliss!

In fact, over time, using the Zibber Zabber became so relaxing I would often fall asleep while using it. A sure sign I carried too much tension in my pelvic floor on those days!

Once I was comfortable with the unit I came out of the bedroom. I started using it every night while lying on the couch watching TV. My husband would joke, "Make sure you don't forget to Zibber Zab your coochie!"

At first I found it embarrassing but soon I was joking too. The positive changes were nothing short of a miracle to me. Within days I was cheering and proudly chatting with Remy about my favorite little gizmo, my Zibber Zabber!

Within a week, my prolapses had noticeably moved up.

A week after that, things were even higher, my perineum was no longer under pressure and the best part? When I did a Kegel things down there actually moved!

After three weeks I started peeing myself. I was devastated. The one thing, the one golden ring I had clung to for so long, was that I rarely ever leaked and definitely did not lose complete bladder control and leak constantly. After a panic filled message to the makers of my Zibber Zabber a very kind and lovely lady told me that it was normal and should right itself in a few days. It was actually a good sign. My organs were so severely prolapsed that I had a kink in my urethra that had been preventing leaking. No ninja skills had been involved in the prevention of leaking, I realized with sadness. I thought this had been one thing I had been good at, where I wasn't damaged. It was a blow to my ego.

Now things were moving up and that kink was straightening out, the nice lady told me I needed to focus on retraining those muscles to control urine flow. And you know what? She was right. A week later the constant leaking stopped and I was back to my normal potty dance routine and frequency issues, which by this point had become such a normal part of life I didn't consider them a huge issue.

One day, about six weeks after starting to use the Zibber Zabber, I was taking the garbage out. Moving those big, heavy bins, especially dragging them through deep snow, was normally painful for me. The action put pressure on my prolapse so I could feel those tissues pushing out. That day I was feeling stronger, and I noticed the pressure was not bothering me. Suddenly, I realized that the bowling ball was not bouncing around with each step.

I set the garbage can down and did a couple of tentative squats.

No pressure.

I did a couple of bunny hops.

I could feel a bit of movement, but not the heavy bounce of the bowling ball that had been my constant companion for so many years.

I ran. Well, jogged for a few steps, then launched into a full run.

Then I laughed, and laughed, and laughed.

Racing inside I called Remy. "The bowling ball is gone!" I cried into the phone when he answered.

"What? What bowling ball?"

"My uterus!"

"What, huh?"

I sighed, mocking exasperation, as I continued to laugh, "You know, when I walk or run I am always complaining about that feeling of the bowling ball bouncing inside me? It's gone!"

"Really? How?"

"The Zibber Zabber!"

"Wow, all hail the Zibber Zabber. That is amazing sweetie." I could hear him smiling down the phone. It was a really great day. That night we celebrated with a cake for desert. Yes, it was that big of a deal. Plus I will take any excuse to have desert.

And the sex, oh beloved sex. The pain went away! My confidence came back. Things were good, things were really, really good. I was a very happy girl with a very happy husband! Was I back to pre-birth status? Nope, things were still different, but now they were a good, working, pain-free different. I was happy to take it and label it a success.

Over the next few months I was able to decrease use of the Zibber Zabber from daily to twice weekly, then twice monthly. After a year of use I continued to use it when I felt things slipping too low or I wanted to prepare my pelvic floor for heavy work like landscaping weekends. What I found most interesting was that I went from using the programs that worked the pelvic floor muscles, to instead using the pelvic floor muscle relaxation programs. Due to the years of tucking in my bum, I often discovered myself swinging back towards a hypertonic pelvic floor. Between maintaining a neutral spine, doing appropriate exercises and running the relaxation eStim programs, I found I could return to a healthy balance quickly and efficiently.

An added bonus, using lubricant with the Zibber Zabber was moisturizing and softening the scar tissues. The scars that caused me so much irritation were becoming less noticeable as the pressure from the prolapses lessened and the scars softened. This was a surprising but welcomed win. I went out and bought myself some soft thongs. I couldn't use them all the time but it was nice to have the option once again.

Finally, I was making progress and finding some serious success. Life changing levels of success.

Going to the Dogs

I am an animal lover. Not sure if that came across earlier in my story, so I will say it again. I love animals. Usually the furry or hairy ones, sometimes feathery or scaly, animals were always part of my life. Growing up I was surrounded by dogs, cats, horses, birds, fish, and not just one of each. Nope, my family believed animals needed companions… or we were just suckers and took in every sob story that came our way. Either way there were always a lot of animals in my life.

When Remy and I bought our first house, I quickly added my first babies into our home, a cat with a serious attitude issue and a dog that we were pretty sure was an Australian dingo that somehow got really lost and ended up in Canada.

Nine years later, shortly before we traveled to Ethiopia to pick up Yonas, my beloved dog passed away. She was my pride and joy. My first child. My happy go lucky girl, with such a zest and love of life.

I was gutted by her loss. With the chaos of going to Ethiopia, then the very difficult adjustment as Yonas settled in and we came to terms with his special needs, it was almost two years before we were ready to add a new dog to the family.

I knew exactly what type of dog I wanted, a large red Doberman. I had owned two red Dobermans as a child and they were amazing companions. I wanted my boys to have the same experience. Remy, well, he had his own ideas. I like big dogs. Hubby wanted a smaller dog. He said it would be less chaos in the house with the boys.

He was being practical again and it usually paid to listen to him when he was being practical. I knew a compromise was needed.

Through an online rescue organization I found a puppy in Mexico. She had the red Doberman coloring, but was small, and likely would be a small to medium sized dog once fully grown. With her perky ears and golden eyes, so sad and lost looking, I knew she was my dog. I named her Lily.

She came home during the Christmas holidays; it was the greatest Christmas present ever according to my boys. From the sunny beaches of Mexico to our Canadian winter was a huge shock for her system, but she was a tough little dog and quickly learned how to snow plow while making her winter sweaters look stylish and fancy.

She grew to be about the size of a Whippet, about twenty-five pounds, with a love of running, playing ball, and hanging out with the kids. She was perfect. She was also exactly what I needed to get off my butt and out the door for some exercise. If I didn't get her out enough she tended to chew things, like the kids' toys, and the utter anguish from the children was enough motivation to get me out exercising her every day.

The boys also learned the importance of cleaning up their toys.

With this new, dog-driven, child-demanded, active lifestyle, I learned about a little thing called limits.

When a part of your body is weak or 'broken', it is always susceptible to injury. Ask anyone that has blown out a knee, torn the ligaments in a shoulder, or damaged their back. They must always be careful to keep those injured areas strong and protected against future injuries.

The same is true of the pelvic floor as I discovered the hard way. Why I have to be so damn pig-headed, I don't know. But it always seems to take me a few lessons before the concept of limits sinks into my brain.

Picture the pelvic floor like a hammock. Now, put a whole bunch of big heavy people on that hammock, see how the hammock bows and hangs low, the connection points straining? Now have those people bounce around on the hammock. Chances are that hammock is going to stretch and eventually break.

Now, apply that concept to the pelvic floor. Instead of people, we have organs (namely the bladder, uterus, rectum, and other tissues). The connection points are ligaments.

Put too much pressure on that floor and BOING! Congratulations, you have now injured your pelvic floor. Welcome to the club.

I did exactly that, one summer day, while I was out hiking with my boys and Lily. The hiking paths around my home are gravel and quite hilly. Far too much for young kids, so I purchased a large double carriage. It was a carriage designed for sporting, active parents that wanted to take along their kids on runs, bike rides or even skiing without worrying about their kids being unable to keep up. Which was exactly what I needed. They could sit and play while I got my workout done.

The thing was balanced beautifully, and easy to push, but it was huge. I had a set route that I would take when I had the boys with me in their carriage. Going this way meant we were always going down the steepest hills. On that summer day we had recently experienced some intense storms. The kind only the prairies can lay claim to with racing bruised skies, sheet lightning, fork lightning, and the kind of thunder that shakes the very foundation of your home. The winds whip around one minute, so intense trees snap and fall with a resounding gunshot crack, then the winds stop, silent, waiting, before hitting again with full vengeance. That summer we had a lot of those storms. The kind that hit hard and fast, but thankfully, leave part of our summer days sunny and enjoyable. During one of those sunny breaks I decided to take the boys in their carriage for a hike. I was getting fitter by the day and craved my daily work outs. Hiking was a great way to feel the burn and work the all-important glutes!

But that day I came across a number of large trees that had been felled by the storms. A number of them crisscrossed, blocking our progress down the path. The trees were too large to move and the brush was too dense to take the carriage around. We were forced to turn back.

Which meant going up the steep hills. One in particular, right near the shores of the local lake, was extremely steep.

I had no choice, I had to push the carriage up the steep gravel hills. I made it up the first two, sweating and panting. Then came the steep hill right by the lake. My boys were happily chatting inside the carriage, squealing with glee as I broke into a jog.

See, my theory was that if I got a run at the hill we could make it up to the top.

It happened half way up the hill. We started sliding backwards, my feet skidding, the carriage slipping on the gravel. I braced against the carriage, trying to stay on my feet and maintain control of the carriage, least it should tumble down the steep bank into the lake.

Somehow, by some super-mom power, I was able to stop the carriage, the children still squealing with excitement.

"This is the best hike ever! Let's do that again!" cried out my boys.

I smiled, my boys had such a joy and love of life, but as I stood bent over, trying to catch my breath I knew something was not quite right. Moments later the pain hit as I tried to move the carriage.

My pelvic floor had failed.

And it wouldn't be the only time.

Much to the disappointment of my children,

I made them walk the rest of the way home. That night I had a bath and rested, sure that everything would be fine in the morning.

The next day it hurt a bit more. I tried to ignore it, my day was busy with runs to preschool and grocery shopping and keeping the kids happy. I kept moving, sure it would sort itself out.

The day after that I was in extreme, debilitating pain.

That pain lasted over a week.

The problem, I discovered, was that my hammock was damaged by the initial incident and every time I would stand up my organs put pressure on that damaged hammock making the injury worse over the course of a few days. Walking anywhere was agonizing. I could barely lift five pounds without sharp shooting pains radiating across the front of my pelvic area.

Moms of young children don't get time off. My boys were constantly on the go and they needed me on the go too. I rested as much as I could but, as any mom can tell you, little ones require a lot of walking, lifting, and bending. And, oh, did bending over hurt!

It took my pelvic floor two agonizing weeks to fully recover.

I learned the hard way I needed to always be aware of protecting my pelvic floor and when I do have an injury, no matter how mild, I need to find ways to rest as much as possible and get the pressure off my pelvic floor so it can heal.

Lesson learned... the hard way!

Sadly, it wouldn't be the last lesson I would learn.

Epic Fail

Why is it that so many lessons hurt? Especially when it comes to your body?

I have an amazing chiropractor that I have been seeing for over twenty years... *yikes*, that makes me old! When I first went to see him it was following a horseback riding accident. I decided to stop the fall from my galloping horse with my face. In retrospect, it was not the smartest way to stop my momentum, especially since I did it into a fence, bouncing my way to the ground as if my head were a giant ball.

Thank goodness I always wore my helmet.

The fall left my face with lots of cuts and soft tissue damage but no broken bones. The doctors assured me I would heal up fine, but then I didn't. For the next few months I lived on a liquid diet, unable to open my jaw more than a few centimetres. Desperate for help I found a chiropractor through recommendations from some friends. He helped heal my TMJ (temporomandibular joint) disorder, relieving much of the pain and getting my jaw moving again, but as with pelvic floor disorders, TMJ is more of a lifelong management issue than a problem that can be fixed. So we developed a steady relationship.

Over the years I continued to see him when my TMJ disorder warranted it, plus whenever I had any other issues requiring a good 'cracking'.

Following my pregnancy my TMJ disorder had been surprisingly good. There were moments of pain but for the most part my jaw was not a major issue.

Then I went to the dentist for a cleaning. What is it with these satanic torture sessions known as dental visits? I know they revel in their evilness.

I knew as I reclined in the blue plastic chair, the bright light in my eyes, that she was taking a very long time and putting a lot of pressure on my jaw, but I thought I could handle it. I was tough and I just wanted it over with already. I had a babysitter waiting for me to get home and I still did not like leaving Yonas for any length of time.

Boy was I wrong. On the drive home things were sore and aching. By the evening the pain was so bad I didn't sleep for the next three days. Even the most powerful painkillers and muscle relaxants did not provide me with any relief. My stomach started revolting from all the pain medications I was taking. I finally caved and went to my chiropractor.

That visit kicked off regular visits for the next two weeks. Sadly our visits involved a lot of pain infliction on me. Not exactly my idea of a great courtship and clandestine affair. Remy doesn't need to worry, he has no competition.

As the chiropractor tried to sort through the jaw issues, I learned how much influence this food munching area has on so many bodily functions. My cognition and mental acuity had been affected, I had hearing loss (and ringing, the ringing in my ears never seemed to stop), vision issues, muscles all over my body were doing strange things and I was exhausted. So exhausted. The kind of exhaustion where each breath is laborious.

Then severe abdominal and pelvic floor pain started. Not my normal prolapse pain, more localized to the front and a constant pain, not the dull ache with shooting pains that I normally enjoyed.

Turns out that as the jaw was going through its adjustments, it was pulling and shifting around on my whole body, as evidenced by my horrid posture as I channeled the hunchback during this time. I would try so hard to get straight, knowing how important it was for my pelvic floor, but it was impossible. I simply could not straighten up and hold a correct posture for more than the briefest of moments.

Remember that song, about how your foot bone is connected to your leg bone? Well it's something like that, about how our whole body is connected. One of the areas my jaw is 'attached' to, and was pulling on, was my transverse abdominals and pelvic floor.

Did I mention all of this happened just before Jace started Kindergarten and Yonas started at a special needs preschool? No? Well it did. Starting new schools is stressful. Adding on all of this, at the same time, was a new level of torture.

Dentists are evil. I'm just saying.

So in the middle of a very chaotic and busy first day of school for both my boys, I went to the chiropractor for another adjustment and he did this thing where he pressed on the attachment points on the inside of my hip bones. He pressed, and pressed, and pressed. Waiting for them to release. Then he yanked on my leg.

I cried. It hurt so badly when he was pressing on the inside of my hips. I broke down. It was some of the most intense pain I have ever experienced.

The muscles on the insides of my legs gave out, I was wobbly and shaky. I could barely walk.

Then the pain and aches started, I felt like someone had slammed me into a wall.

I wanted to hate my chiropractor. I wanted to punch him. But the torture was actually helping.

Happily, in the face of all of this pain and discomfort, I could feel my body healing and getting back in balance, but it was a process. A very long and difficult process. My chiro warned me on our first visit after the dentist that it was going to be a rough go.

Damn, I hated it when he was right. Thankfully within a couple of months I was back on my feet, butt out, spine aligned, pain free, and taking on the world again.

Oh, and still hating the dentist.

Hula Hoops and Jogging

Being free of the bowling ball was a major turning point for me, physically and emotionally. I felt so strong, whole and healthy. I wanted to do everything, anything. I didn't realize how shackled my life had been by that bowling ball until the shackles came off. For the first time in years, I felt free.

The first thing I started doing was increasing my workouts. I added power walking and intense hiking. My boys were getting older by this point and were no longer interested in carriage rides but walking with them was not conducive to exercise. For a toddler it is about the journey! Stopping to smell every weed, examining every rock, chasing every butterfly.

The need to exercise was becoming intense. It just felt so damn good. My body was finally working, my muscles growing, my body stronger. I found myself getting short and snappy with my boys when I couldn't satisfy this need.

So a new plan was born. Every night, after the kids were tucked into bed, I would take off for a quick power walk or hike while Remy dealt with the boys and their sleep procrastination attempts.

"I'm thirsty."

"I need to go pee."

"There's a strange shadow."

The list went on and on, a battle cry familiar to parents everywhere. Well that battle was now up to Remy to fight. I needed some time to get out of the house and work out.

The rest of my workouts, including doing squats, stretches, yoga and light weights, would continue to be done in small increments while taking care of the children.

While playing with the boys I discovered that hula hooping really helped me build my core without any pressure or discomfort on my pelvic floor. Do you know how long my kids can play with hula hoops? Every day I easily kept them occupied with their own brightly colored circles for at least fifteen minutes while I hula hooped my way to a stronger core.

Plus, hula hooping was fun. It made me feel young again. It made me giggle. Especially when my boys would try and do tricks and silly things with their hoops. I realized I didn't do enough giggling anymore. So I did more hula hooping. And more giggling.

At one point I tried those weighted cuffs that go around your ankles and wrists. It only lasted a week. Not only did they chafe but I kept forgetting I was wearing them while running around and would end up tripping and fall on my face. Coordination has never been a talent of mine.

One night I was gliding down the stairs, clenching my glutes with each step, trying to make myself so light I couldn't feel any impact. I had the cuffs on. I slipped. I bounced down the stairs on my butt. My tailbone hurt for days. I got rid of the weighted cuffs and never wore them again.

As my fitness increased I tried to increase the difficulty, picking tougher routes, steeper hills, walking faster, pumping my arms, but after a while none of it was enough. Walking simply only does so much for the body. I needed to crank up the intensity. I talked to a number of pelvic floor specialists and physiotherapists. All of them advised that the best way to increase intensity was to lengthen the time of my workouts.

My evening workouts were short, only thirty minutes. My boys wanted Mommy around while they were trying to sleep and would wait up anxiously until they heard me come back. Plus, I wanted to spend my evenings with my husband. It was hard enough to find time alone with each other; that precious couple of hours after the kids were in bed was important. It was our time to chat, to connect and find out what was happening in each other's lives. So lengthening my workouts was not an option.

What I needed was intensity to get the most out of the short window of time I could dedicate.

So, despite the advice of all the professionals, one warm summery night I broke into a gentle jog. It was more of a shuffle really. Moments later, for the first time in ages, I started sweating.

Learning to run with a prolapse was a very slow and gradual process. At first I did barely more than a bouncy walk, then I jogged for ten paces, then back to a walk, then ten more tentative jogging paces, then walk. With each step I was listening to my body, looking for pressure or waiting for that bowling ball to make a reappearance.

I am sure I looked a bit loonie, starting and stopping. Thankfully I had my young dog with me, so I made it look like I was doing all these weird start and stops because I was training her. Not because my uterus was falling out or anything. You know, in case that neighbor twitching her curtains was wondering.

Now I didn't disagree with the professionals who said 'no running'. Living with POP for many years had demonstrated to me all the truths that they repeated over and over again. I knew gravity and impact were my enemies when it came to keeping my prolapsed organs up. Plus, I'm not stupid; I had come so far, and those setbacks hurt, physically and mentally. The last thing I wanted was to hurt myself temporarily or even permanently. I still had my eye set on the end goal - no surgery until after menopause.

But I also needed to live my life. I needed to feel capable, strong, whole. I wanted to feel like I could achieve something physical. Even though I had never been a runner, running was suddenly what I wanted more than anything.

Most of all I wanted my dignity back. I was sure this path would help me. So I set out once again to find something to help make my dream of running possible.

A trip to the fitness store resulted in a new set of runners that were designed to minimize impact and a pair of shorts that made it look like I was wearing a diaper. Thankfully, they came with a set of loose board shorts to wear over the top to hide their ugliness.

The diaper shorts were actually bike rider compression shorts. The diaper part provided support between my legs and padding. The compression feature kept everything snugged up, firmly in place.

I set out on a run that night in my fancy new gear. It was good, better than before the new gear, but I still felt the need to have something inside me to help stabilize the tissues that I could feel moving with each step. There was no way I could use the pessary. I couldn't walk without it falling and irritating me. I decided to search natural alternatives to pessaries and came across sea sponges. They could be cut to fit any body shape but were soft enough to fit snuggly without pressure. As an added bonus, they could be used as a monthly feminine product. I was sold and ordered four with rush delivery.

They arrived three days later.

I am not sure what I expected but I was a bit surprised to see they looked exactly like smaller versions of the sponges we bathed with as children.

They were also rock hard.

The instructions said to wet the sponge first before inserting. I stood at the sink, letting the water darken the sponge as it soaked in. Finally, a couple of tentative squeezes reassured me that the sponge had indeed softened up and become nice and squishy. So standing with one leg raised, my foot balanced on the edge of the tub, I slid it in.

It was cold!

From then on I always used warm, almost hot water.

But it pushed all the tissues up. Best of all, they stayed up.

I did a few squats then a few jumping jacks.

It stayed in place. Even better, it stayed in place without any pain.

I wore it the rest of the day. Over long periods of time it would sometimes slip, but the results were a landslide victory over the blue donut of torture pessary.

That night I made sure everything was tucked up nice and high behind the sea sponge. I pulled on my compression shorts, strapped on my runners, and set off.

I jogged for twenty minutes straight, no walking breaks, and came back red-faced and sweaty.

It was AWESOME.

And Then I Ran

One of the things I had noted as my fitness increased was that my greatest improvements in my prolapse symptoms came from when I built up my glutes, along with doing Kegels.

So the next night I tried something new. At that stage I was a big advocate of trying everything, no matter how weird or strange!

As I jogged, every third step I would squeeze a quick Kegel then with the next step I would flex my butt. I am sure if anyone was paying close attention they would wonder what the heck I was doing. It was not proper jogging form.

But it felt good.

I added in a little stretch and flex of my

abdominals as I jogged, ensuring my transverse abdominals were engaged the way I had learned from a video. It took a few minutes before I entered a nice steady rhythm. Gently squeezing a different muscle group with each step.

I found I had to keep the movements subtle or I would strike down with too much impact and jar myself, but small little flexes and movements made a big difference. It also forced me to keep my pace gentle and slow.

Well, most of the time.

I was a mother, after all, with two little boys who loved to push buttons.

One rainy night, after a day of dealing with temper tantrums and meltdowns, I really needed to burn off some steam.

As I stepped out into the rain I thought 'screw it' and took off in a run. I didn't care about my prolapse or working specific muscles. At that moment I wanted to just run. Run away. Run fast. Run.

So I ran. Hard. Fast. Listening to nothing but the rhythmic beating of my feet.

I turned onto the gravel hiking trails with the steep hills.

And I ran.

I rolled my ankle on the gravel.

I kept running.

Limping, soaked in sweat and panting worse than Lily, I came home thirty minutes later.

I was also grinning from ear to ear.

It may not have been smart, given my body's limits, but it had felt damn good.

That night I made sure to use my Zibber Zabber on a relaxation program and had a long soak in a warm bath.

The next morning I hurt. Mostly it was muscle hurts but I had to admit to myself that part of the hurt was also inside. My pelvic floor had taken a bit of a beating. That day I rested and in the evening I took it easy during my workout, only walking for a short time.

By the next morning I felt good again.

I wanted to scream from the rooftops. I was running!

Not only was I running but I was biking. My boys had discovered bikes. What is it about kids and new things that make them obsess and want to do the same thing over and over again?

Don't get me wrong, I was ecstatic. I had fond memories of riding my bike with my parents. I proudly rode my pink banana-seat bike with the flag and spoke beads clickety-clacking as I went down the road. My parents rode on a double bike because my mom never learned how to ride, so she sat behind my dad, griping with white knuckles, pretending she was enjoying herself. Later on I rode with my friends, going on amazing adventures along the trails that wound through our neighborhood.

My bike was my childhood portal to fun and I was so happy my boys had discovered biking!

I was also happy because this was just another sign my boys were getting bigger. I rarely needed to carry them anymore (unless faced with PTSD episodes) and if they could ride their own bikes it meant I no longer needed to haul the trailer behind my bike, which was a huge relief to me and my pelvic floor. Pulling that bike trailer was hard work.

I wanted to encourage their enthusiasm so I dusted off my banana yellow bike (no banana seat) and we set off on our first family bike ride. Things were good. My bike was equipped with a special gel seat that was open through the middle. I purchased it specifically to minimize pressure and irritation on my prolapse and scars. I was ready to ride!

We rode for two hours on the first day. The next day they were ready to go again for another hour. Then again the next day. Even with my special seat, things hurt. Having that much pressure and weight on my perineum for so long made things feel very bruised.

But not 'prolapse' hurt. It was the hurt that came from irritated scars, tender tissues, and doing something new.

Speaking of new, I was so emboldened by my new fitness success that I decided to join my son on the hill that winter. At only seven years old, he was already an avid snowboarder. He loved the sport and took regular lessons. I decided I would join him on the bunny hill.

I had tried skiing once or twice in my life, enough to demonstrate a complete lack of natural talent, but I had never been snowboarding.

I spent two hours on the hill.

The good news was that my prolapse did not bother me at all.

The bad news - my knees swelled up to double their normal size and were black for over a week. Oh and my wrists! I broke every single fall, and there were a lot of them, with my knees and wrists. My prolapse may not have bothered me but I decided to leave snowboarding to my seven year old expert. I would cheer him on from the chalet. I was too old for that kind of beating!

Anyway that wasn't the point. I never intended to become a snowboarding phenom. The idea was simply to support my son. To be active with him. To role model a brave, active lifestyle so that he would grow up into a man who embraces fitness, health and bravery. I didn't want him to remember his mother sitting on the sidelines. I wanted him to remember how funny it was when Mom kept falling on her face that time she tried to snowboard!

In that respect, the experience was a complete

success.

It was also a sign that my life was changing. Significantly. No longer was I scared, isolated, fearful. I was comfortable, hopeful, confident and embracing life.

Life was changing significantly in another area as well. After many, many, false starts, we finally found a therapist that was able to help Yonas. The therapy involved farm animals, including dogs, chickens, bunnies, lamas and horses. My equestrian, animal loving heart, fully approved of the nature inspired program. My momma heart was elated to see how the animals healed my son, showing him a world that was not to be feared but embraced, cherished, and enjoyed. My son was happy and confident for the first time. This was the boy I had known was buried under the trauma for so many years. It was amazing to finally see him living life like a typical preschooler.

I was overjoyed. My excitement for life and hope for the future became my new normal.

My body was changing too.

Like most women, I had never lost the last five pounds after giving birth. Not only did I lose that five pounds but I kept going, losing a total of twenty pounds, taking me back to my wedding day weight.

I felt amazing.

I bought all new clothes, including tons of

cute dresses. I felt confident. I felt beautiful. I felt strong.

The darkness and depression had finally lifted.

I felt free of the shackles POP and depression had placed on me for so many years.

PART 5

LIVING LIFE

Living With Prolapse

In retrospect, now the darkness of depression has receded, I have realized that one of the side effects of living with a severe case of pelvic organ prolapse was a loss of confidence and fear.

It was exhausting to live in a constant state of fear.

It was hard to be a strong, confident woman, comfortable in my body, when I was in constant pain, when I spent every moment, especially in public, worried about leaking urine or leaking during my cycle with no warning. It was hard to have any confidence when I couldn't rely on the one thing I needed to rely on the most, my body. I simply could not trust it anymore.

For me, this loss of confidence spilled over

into all areas of my life. I left my career permanently due to a combination of factors, but one of the main reasons was pelvic organ prolapse. If you had asked me, before Jace was born, what kind of mother would I be, what my five year plan held, there was absolutely no way I would have predicted that I would be a stay-at-home mom who abandoned her career and became relatively unfit.

It took a lot of work to rebuild my confidence. To finally become comfortable in this new body, this new life.

Life changed so much after giving birth. It wasn't supposed to. Strong, modern, super-moms did not give up anything. Being a mother simply became another thing on the plate, but nothing about *me* was supposed to change.

But it did change. Completely. I wasn't prepared for the change. I didn't want all these changes. I grieved for my old life, my old body. I had to give myself the grace and space to go through that grieving process, to understand that it was part of healing.

The only way to become whole, healthy and strong again was to heal more than my body, I had to heal my mind and heart as well.

What I needed to learn was that different does not mean worse, it was just different; I could still be the confident, strong, beautiful woman I wanted to be.

Should I have looked into therapy? Maybe. I am pretty sure it would have helped on some level. Thankfully, due to my background in psychology and all the studying and work I was doing to help Yonas with his issues, including going to his counseling sessions, meant that in a way I was getting therapy. It was not a conventional approach, but helping Yonas heal helped me heal, and I thank him every day for coming into our lives.

Things really do happen for a reason. Sometimes it takes a really long time for that reason to become evident, which can be so frustrating. Learning to let go and trust is hard.

Another thing that helped with my confidence was those little sea sponges. Not only did they work as great pessaries when needed, but they also functioned as tampons. For years I had avoided taking my boys swimming; heck, for three days every month I avoided leaving the house, period (ha ha! Love the unintentional pun!). Traveling? It was a nightmare.

Before giving birth I traveled all the time. Now the idea of possibly having my cycle while traveling was enough to put off any thoughts I had of taking a trip. The pill was great at helping regulate my cycle but I found my body rebelled when I would try and change my cycle using the pills.

But then I started using the sea sponges. I

could travel without any worry about my cycle. I could go swimming almost any day of the month. The heaviest days were still out, but any other day was fair game. I take my boys swimming all the time. And you know what? Being in the water when my pelvic floor is stressed or tired feels fantastic. All that weight and pressure just lifts off my damaged tissues. Now I have a way of getting some relief whenever I need it.

Living with severe POP is a matter of balance. Balancing the needs of my body against my needs as a person, mother and woman. How that balance is achieved is the puzzle that can never be fully completed. The pieces keep moving and changing. There is no cure for prolapse. Even surgery requires ongoing care and upkeep.

The Cervix Challenge

The biggest impact on my quality of life was my cervix. It was my cervix that constantly popped out of my body and my cervix that was extremely sensitive to eStim, hence why I would eStim lying down and with my hips propped. I needed that annoying cervix up and out of the way!

I went to see my family doctor once for my yearly physical and Pap smear. We talked extensively during the exam about my prolapse issues. She didn't have much to add and I felt like I was educating her on POP, which is probably not far from the truth. I told her how my cervix is often right at the opening or just outside of my vagina. So she knew my status before strapping me into the stirrups and pulling out that nasty metal contraption they use for Pap smears. I have noticed that since I gave birth to Jace the speculum is extremely uncomfortable, and often very painful, probably due to muscle and nerve damage.

She spent ten minutes down there, pushing the speculum around painfully inside of me. After a couple of minutes she said, "I'm having a hard time finding your cervix. Has anyone ever told you, you have a tilted uterus?"

"Um, I just told you I that I have severe pelvic organ prolapse."

"Yes, but I can't find your cervix."

With a roll of my eyes I had to guide her through doing a Pap on me. I told her to remove the speculum and to look right inside the opening. The speculum was blocking my cervix, which was right there at the opening.

"Wow, I have never seen a cervix there before," she said in shock.

"Um, yeah, that would be what I meant when I said I have *a severe case of pelvic organ prolapse.* My uterus is falling out of my body and the cervix is leading the charge. My other organs are making a break for it too, but I don't think you need to check those today."

"Well, have you looked into surgery? A hysterectomy perhaps? I could refer you to a surgeon."

Insert teeth gnashing and hair pulling here.

Finding good medical care for prolapse is insanely hard. I am not sure if it is this hard everywhere, but around here very few doctors know about prolapse.

I often felt that I was in an epic battle with my cervix. It was on one side of the abyss, storming towards my vaginal opening, and I stood on the other side, armed with a Zibber Zabber and a sea sponge, declaring, "Thou shall not pass!"

Sometimes I won. Other times I lost and was pulled into the abyss.

The cervix is a very hard piece of round tissue, about the size of a quarter, at the entrance to your uterus. In a healthy, natural state, it should be up, nice and high, inside the vaginal canal. When you have a severe uterine prolapse, that hard, sensitive bit is either trying to push its way out of your vagina or is completely on the outside of your vagina, rubbing against your underwear. Nice, hey?

The cervix is also extremely sensitive. I mentioned earlier that eStim and the cervix are not a good mix. When they touch it was like a lightning strike on my insides. The pain and burning unbelievable. Not only that, but any pushing or pressure against the cervix can be extremely painful. This means the very items that are helping to push things back up (pessary or sea sponges), could cause pain. Sometimes, when my uterine prolapse was really acting up, it would press down on my perineum and create pelvic pain that would radiate like a spider's web through my pelvic area.

It took a lot of time and introspection to learn the source of certain types of pelvic pain, a skill worth mastering as it helped me pinpoint what was out of balance so I could pick the most effective treatment. For instance, as soon as my tailbone would start to hurt I knew my pelvic floor was becoming hypertonic again and I needed to do the relaxation program on my Zibber Zabber and some relaxing squats. Lower back pain meant my prolapses were pulling down and I needed to do things to help lift them up, such as using a sea sponge.

The pain originating from my cervix became very easy to recognize once I made the connection, it would radiate through my whole abdominal cavity, kind of like a tooth ache. The pain may start in the tooth but it can radiate through your jaw and face. Often I would need to weigh my options and determine which treatment plan would be the least painful that day, based on the position of my cervix.

Learning about my body, recognizing what was causing pain, all became part of finding that all important balance.

I often thought that if I could just get rid of

my cervix, life would be a lot easier. I was living with the prolapses, but my cervix caused most of my pain and aggravation.

The good news is that over time, my cervix moved up inside and generally started staying in there. Unless I did something dumb, like building a rock wall. Which, of course, I did. And paid the price. Sigh.

Have I mentioned I can be a slow learner at times?

Traveling With POP

Another facet of living with POP is that air pressure changes can affect my prolapse. On a day to day basis I rarely noticed anything but when I would fly my prolapse would fall, which inevitably made for a much more uncomfortable and painful trip. I considered bringing my Zibber Zabber on numerous trips but I always worried about carrying it in my luggage. I have had airport security workers freak out about toothpaste. What would they do if they saw my Zibber Zabber? I may feel like a bolder, braver me, but airport security still scares me. I really did not want to be explaining my Zibber Zabber or having some security worker pawing it and playing with it if they searched my suitcase. Some things are just way beyond my comfort zone.

I once tried flying with a sea sponge in but I found the sponge put pressure on my bladder and having to go to the washroom every thirty minutes while in an airplane, with my children, was just not a good fit.

I have yet to find a way to make traveling easier. Prolapse issues have simply become an expected part of my travels and I spend a lot of time doing my exercises before and during my trips. Leading up to any trips, I also make sure I use my Zibber Zabber every day for at least a week. That usually gets things really nice and high, which limits the impact of any slipping due to flying.

It's far from perfect, but it's livable.

When I travel, though, the desire for surgery sometimes raises its head. It is then, when my schedule is thrown off and my arsenal of POP therapies are unavailable, that I feel the draw to a more permanent fix.

I just wish I was sure it would be a permanent fix and not a temporary plaster, or worse yet, a new kind of damage. A new kind of struggle.

Balance

Living with prolapse has become easier and easier as time passes. It has been almost eight years since Jace's birth, and I no longer think about prolapse every day. I wish I could never think about it again, but I have accepted that it is not my reality. Even if I do have surgery I will need to adjust my lifestyle, once again to accommodate yet another new reality, a new body.

I am not ready for that yet.

I have heard amazing success stories with surgery. I have also heard the most horrid of horror stories with surgery.

Right now, I have a handle on my prolapses. I have made accommodations, I have made changes, and I have a lifestyle that fits the needs of my prolapses, the needs of my family, and my needs as a woman and person.

One day, living with POP will become more difficult. It is a given. Gravity and age are the enemies in this battle. I have mentioned before that the goal is balance; balance that creates a healthy mind, body and spirit. I will continue to try new things and work to maintain a healthy balance. If I reach a stage where I can no longer live with POP, using the tools and treatments available to me, then I will start to research surgery options.

I will not go with the surgeon I saw years ago. Instead I will travel to a different surgeon; perhaps one who is willing to try a less invasive technique. Definitely one who is more confident about their success rates. It will cost money and time, but investing in myself is important. So, when the time is right, I will take the next steps towards achieving a new healthy balance living with POP.

And the best part? I know Remy, Jace and Yonas will be right by my side. My boys. My rocks. My loves.

Grief and Depression

I am sure by now it is obvious one of my biggest struggles throughout this new life with POP has been depression and grief, which manifested as frustration and anger at times.

For me it was not just the presence of depression in my life, but the never-ending morphing of that depression. From sadness to frustration, to shame and grief, to anger. My emotions, at times, became so toxic they were affecting everyone around me.

Although this has been a journey with POP, it has also been a journey with depression.

The very traumatic birth of my son left me with so much pain. Then there was the rollercoaster of hormones and first time mother jitters, as I struggled with a body that seemed so very foreign to me for that first year after Jace's birth. A year that ended with a diagnosis of severe pelvic organ prolapse and spending half a day every week in uro-physiotherapy.

I consider it a blessing that I always wanted to adopt. The adoption process gave me hope. Gave me strength. Especially during the second and third years postpartum, as I struggled with very messy menstrual cycles, excruciating pain and spasms, all while I tried to balance working and a toddler. Having such a positive, bright focus in the adoption helped me pull through.

After Yonas came home, and his intense needs became evident, I hit my darkest moments. I was dealing with my own disability, and finding the energy to care for a son with severe disabilities often felt like an insurmountable obstacle.

Thank goodness I had my boys, who kept me moving and gave me hope for the future. For every struggle my boys faced, they also showed an immense amount of tenacity, hope, grit and determination. What Yonas endured, before coming to our family, was beyond what any baby should face; yet he kept moving forward, trying to heal and get better. But he needed me to help him heal and, through that process, I noticed my passions starting to revive.

I had a son who needed serious support and

healing; with my background in psychology, I had the knowledge to help him, but I needed to learn more skills. As I started to learn more, I noticed I started healing, and my son started healing. They were tiny, itty bitty, teeny weeny steps, but steps they were. Every tiny step was one step closer to healing, health and happiness. I just had to focus on that one baby step and not get lost in the many miles still left to travel.

I also consider it a great blessing that the adoption process brought the needs of mothers in the developing world to my attention. Fighting back against the depression became possible once I realized how other women live. It provided me with some much needed perspective. A perspective that gave me the strength to fight against the depression and POP, allowing me to regain control of my life. It also gave me hope. After seeing what these women had overcome, it gave me hope that I could overcome my own obstacles.

The issue of grief and prolapse did not always come in ways I expected. Approximately six years postpartum, we had a horrible Christmas. My grandmother suffered a stroke while alone in her apartment. She was not discovered for twenty-four hours. She lived another three weeks in a coma before she passed away. Only eight months before her passing, my husband's grandfather also passed away. Death and loss is hard on kids. When you have children sensitized to death and loss through adoption, it becomes even more so.

I tried to continue sleeping and eating well, but my stomach was often tied in knots of grief. I wanted to take all the pain and loss from my children - doesn't every mother? About two weeks after Christmas, my jaw and pelvic floor started causing me a lot of pain.

I went to my amazing chiropractor, who, that day, also functioned as therapist. He helped me to see that my body was completely exhausted but it was doing what it needed to help me process the grief. Just as it would with any other injury, the emotional injuries I was suffering from were making themselves known at my two weakest points, my jaw and my pelvic floor.

It was a hard time but also a great reminder that my body is not a bunch of individual pieces. My mind and body are all part of a whole that works together in perfect balance. Well, most of the time. Those times when I fell out of balance I needed to work at regaining a healthy balance of all my parts. Only then would I be back to enjoying true health of my whole being.

Similar issues would happen if I became sick. I dreaded developing a cold with any sort of cough or sneezing. Without fail my cervix would end up outside of my body due to lack of exercise and the constant force on my pelvic floor from sneezing and coughing. Seeing it hanging was like a punch in the chest each time. To make so much progress, only to feel like I had lost it all and was starting from square one again. It was devastating, each and every time.

The fear was that perhaps this time the damage was too severe. Perhaps I wouldn't be able to bring my body back. Perhaps I wasn't going to make my goal of waiting until after menopause for surgery.

As if the universe knew what I needed, I would always get a new article or charity update, or my boys would do something to inspire me. There was always something to remind me that I am strong enough to fight back, I am strong enough to do it again. And I did. Each and every time. And with time, the healing process became a little shorter, a little faster with each cycle of re-healing. They were small improvements, only noticeable to me after the passage of time, but they were there.

The fear, though, that perhaps this time I wouldn't come back, that I wouldn't heal, that fear continues to this day.

The Trouble With Trauma

Trauma is a tricky thing. It sticks with you, raising its ugly head when you least expect it. It has been eight years and I still struggle when I see friends or family pregnant. Some have listened to my struggles. They understand and ask intelligent questions. I feel that I can talk with them openly, honestly, without feeling that I am screaming into a brick wall. They want to know what happened to me and what they can do to protect themselves. We can have great conversations, where I feel like women are finally starting to get it.

Then there are other women who, 'don't want to hear any horror stories'. I keep my mouth shut; I don't share unless asked, but all I can think about is that day at my friend's house, when his wife pulled me to the side and whispered in my ear.

I wish I had taken the time to sit down. That I had talked with her. Asked her what she meant and what I could do. I wish I had trusted in the knowledge that had been offered willingly, and honestly, by a woman who had gone before me and knew things I did not.

I wish I could protect all my family and friends. I would not wish prolapse on anyone but, as with anything, I especially want to protect those I love. Sadly, I can't force anyone to listen. All I can do is hope that they have beautiful deliveries, resulting in beautiful babies, and their bodies return to their beautiful pre-pregnancy state. That what has happened to me, and so many other women, will bypass them.

One day I was hanging out on a social media website and one of my 'online' friends, who was a photographer, posted asking about birth photography. Yes, as in having a stranger present throughout the birthing process, taking pictures. She insinuated that one of the biggest regrets for most mothers was that this 'special moment' had not been recorded, minute by minute, and preserved in high resolution detail for all of eternity.

My response was akin to the transition of a werewolf. Kind, loving human in one breath, then vicious, slobbering, angry beast in the next.

I started out trying to bite my tongue, "Not all births are a beautiful experience. Many women have very traumatic births, that they wish they could forget, let alone allowing a stranger to witness and record."

She replied, perky and oblivious that she was poking a beast born from birth trauma. "But all mothers treasure the day their baby came into the world! It is a special, once in a lifetime moment that you can never capture again!"

I am sure she probably included some sideways happy faces in there.

The snarling began, slobber splattering over the keyboard. "What, like the eight hours I spent standing naked in a shower, puking my guts out? Yeah, those were moments I want to cherish but we could replicate it this weekend, if you wish. A few bottles of wine and I should be good to go."

I wasn't done. The beast had taken over in all its vicious nastiness. "Or would you like to capture the moment when the doctor ripped my body to shreds as she yanked my son from my body? Or perhaps when the nurse pressed on my stomach and blood shot across the room, coating the wall and half the room in blood? That would be a great shot. Perhaps you could sell it, or post it all over the internet, as photographers like to do as they promote themselves. I am sure some B rate horror flick director would love to use it to promote his film. Yeah, that would be great."

Teeth bared, I went for the jugular. "I don't need a photographer to remind me of my son's birth. I live with pain and complications from that delivery every single day. Having photos of the event would be like you taking photos of a severe car crash I was in, that left me severely disabled, then giving them to me in a fancy album like some cherished gift. No thanks. Cameras and strangers can stay the hell away from my delivery room. It's just asking for trouble."

Then I chickened out and deleted everything I wrote without posting it.

A month later she started posting her birth photography pictures all over my feed. Mother's sweaty and straining. Slimy newborns being pulled from their mothers' bodies. Women collapsed, exhausted, their new babies lying on their chest.

Each of those photos was like a kick in the gut. They sent my blood pressure rising, my body breaking out into a sweat. Each image was a nasty reminder of my horrible experience.

One of the things I have learned through helping my son cope with post traumatic stress disorder is that you can not control the instinctual fight or flight reactions, but you can control your environment and remove as many triggers as possible.

I recognized the signs of fight or flight. The feelings of helplessness, anger, panic, fear - all triggered by those photos.

I needed to protect myself.

So I made the choice between a distant friend or my own health and happiness. The choice was easy, just as it has always been easy to do what I needed to do to protect my son from his traumas.

I deleted her from my friend list.

Super-Mom

Before I became a mother I saw signs of a phenomenon, one I like to call the Super-mom Syndrome. You know the type, maybe you are that type (redemption is possible!). It is the mom who insists everything is perfect, everything is wonderful. If you go to their house they will have food prepared, the toys neatly organized, they will talk about all the projects they are doing, their job, their charity work, the sports programs for their kids, all the homeschooling or homework they do with the kids, their latest diet craze inspired menu plans for the next sixty days, and on and on.

They are self-proclaimed, although maybe untitled, super-moms. They want you to think they are amazing and perfect. They have everything together. They are a super-mom.

The problem is that it is not true; as moms, we all struggle and we all have our battles. Life is not perfect and, although I definitely do not think we need to focus on the negatives, creating this false image of over the top perfection is not doing anyone any favors.

For a long time I suffered quietly with my prolapse. I tried to pretend everything was perfect. No matter how much it hurt, no matter how far out my damn cervix was hanging, I plastered on a smile, picked up my kids, carried those heavy groceries, went to those postnatal bootcamp, kick your ass programs, I did home renovations, I did it all.

Absolutely nothing was wrong, everything was perfect. I had everything under control.

That day I couldn't comfort my son when he was scared of my friend's dogs, when I watched her comfort him. That was the day I gave up on the super-mom ideal. Faking it 'til I made it was not working and it was actually hurting me. It was time to drop it.

The other thing I had to accept was that I was raw and vulnerable. It often felt like people were judging me, that they were living at me. It was a very self centered way of thinking but when other mothers would do things, I would internalize it as a slight against me. They dropped all their pregnancy weight and joined intense bootcamps, only six months after giving birth, to show me up, to hurt me. They went on fabulous trips, to hurt me. They did things only to rub it in my face that I could not do them too.

For some reason, I kept thinking people were doing things to show off and hurt me. That, for some reason, I was the motivation for their actions, or they were at least passing judgment with their actions. I was hurting so much. I started interpreting people's actions in a way that caused me pain, without ever really considering the real drive behind their actions.

It is weird how depression distorts reality.

Realizing the issue was with no one other than me was hard. Admitting I was wrong, had been wrong for years, was hard. It took time.

In retrospect, the idea that any mother has time to do anything other than get through her days is laughable.

Depression is a tricky beast.

It messes with you.

These lessons were tough to learn, but life can be hard, and with each lesson I was learning more about how to live with POP. And living with POP was something I had committed myself to; and if there is one thing I don't like to do, it's break a commitment. I wanted, no I *needed,* to see this through. At almost seven years postpartum I was not only living with POP but, most of the time, I was no longer thinking of POP either. I was living life happily. Something depression had tried to trick me into thinking was an impossible dream.

The one thing that got me through even the worst days was love. I am so extremely blessed to have the most amazing men in my life. Remy loves me, even on my worst days. When I am snarky, when I am sad, when I am lost. All he has ever wanted for me was happiness and he has encouraged me, every step of the way, to find that happiness, however possible.

One of my dreams was to write stories. When it became evident I would not be rejoining the workforce, he encouraged me to start writing. Cheering me on at every step, no matter how small, even when I told him I would be writing about my privates. In fact, he is the reason I had the nerve to share my story. Without his support and encouragement, I couldn't have been so open, so brutally honest. He has always been my greatest source of inspiration and love.

My beautiful and amazing boys, Jace and Yonas. They can drive me to insanity and drive me to great acts of bravery. I do all that I do to be a better person for them.

I am here. I may be broken, but I am here and I want to be the best mother I can be. One of the ways I can do that is by being involved and modeling a healthy, active lifestyle. I love my boys so much; I want the absolute best for them and will do everything in my power for them to achieve their greatest dreams.

I thought being a good mom meant sacrificing myself for these goals, for my children, for my family. Giving up on me, to focus only on them. I am not sure when it happened but, over time, I realized that what my boys and Remy want most of all is not my sacrifices, they want me. Happy, healthy, whole. Me.

So simple and obvious, but it took me so long to see it. To understand it.

Most of all, I have learned that getting through the grief, and past the depression, is about loving myself. With all my lumps and bumps, scars and broken bits, I need to wake up every morning, look in the mirror - I mean seriously look in the mirror - and say that I love myself. I love what I am doing. I love where I am going. I love how I am living. I love who I am. Right now. Today. In this moment.

Love gives me the will to get up each day and live fuller.

It seems so obvious, yet it took me years to realize that I didn't love myself. I didn't love this new 'mother' version of myself. By learning to love myself again, opening my heart to myself, it led me to healing.

A Letter to Me

They say hindsight is twenty-twenty. I often believe that if we could live life in reverse we would live more fully, more completely, with more intention. But it is those struggles, those obstacles, those challenges, that push us to the sharp edge that carves us into greater humans.

Looking back, I wish someone had taken me under their wing. A fairy godmother, of sorts. Someone to listen, support, provide guidance and hope. Someone who knew everything about this condition and what could be done to help me. A hand to help guide me through the dark days and lift that veil of depression, so I could see more clearly.

Perhaps the best fairy godmother for my

newly postpartum self, would be my current self. After all, who knows me best?

If I could send a letter from my current self to my newly postpartum self, it would read like this:

Dear Postpartum Me - Eight Years Ago,

I know you are so stressed right now. Your heart is beating a million miles a minute, and I know the fear that is clutching at you. Even from this distance I can still remember the feel of those claws of fear digging in. To be honest, there are times when those claws reach out for me even now.

You just had your beautiful baby boy a few months ago. He is gorgeous, with spiky black hair and blond tips.

Right now it is hard, your beautiful little boy is so cute, but you are hurting so much, more than you have ever hurt in your life. The birth aftermath hurts more than any labor contraction.

I know your labor did not go as you wished. That beautiful boy, well he got stuck and they finally had to rip him from your body. It saved his life (and yours, as you will come to realize one day), but now your body is damaged in ways you did not even know were possible.

I know the words 'pelvic organ prolapse' are scary. I know those bulges are also scary, but please do not let this consume you. Do not let anger, bitterness or frustration become your shield in life.

See this moment is a defining moment in your life. In part due to this diagnosis you are going to pursue an amazing, life altering journey to your second son. Your life path will be forever altered for the better. I know it does not seem that way right now, but trust me. I have seen the future, and it's good.

Do not let this get you down. Do not let the anger, bitterness or frustration get the better of you. You are better than this. You are stronger than this.

It will be hard, in so many ways, but I know you. I have faith in you. You will come away from this stronger, better and more beautiful than before.

One day, when you are at your lowest, years from now, you will even discover new ways of caring for your body that will significantly reduce your symptoms. It is possible. Have faith in your willpower. Have faith in your intelligence. Have faith in your dedication. And, most of all, have faith in your body.

Life is good. Focus on the good, believe in your own power. Let go and trust that all that happens is for the greater good. You may not understand it now, but take a breath, let it go, and trust that it is good. One day the bigger picture will be revealed.

A smooth journey will never challenge you, it is boring, and will not push you to keep pursuing that which makes life better. This part of the path is rough, it has lots of twists and turns and branches. But the view from the other end is worth it. Push on, one foot in front of the other, and keep your eyes on the horizon.

Be prepared; there will be a lot of judgments and accusations. They will sting. Boy, they will sting. POP can make you feel so raw. So vulnerable. You will hear that the reason you have POP is your own fault:

You do not have proper posture.

You work out wrong.

You have a job that is damaging your pelvic floor.

You eat wrong.

You do too many Kegels, or not enough Kegels, or are just doing them all wrong.

You are too stressed.

You do too much.

You are not doing enough.

You don't know enough.

You sit, move, walk, run, breathe wrong.

There is a ton of advice out there. Some of it will help. Some of it will hurt. Take those bits that help and forget the rest. None of that matters, what matters is getting you healthy and strong. Focus only on those things that help you reach your goal.

Hang in there. I love you and our little wayward child of a uterus. It may not seem like it, but this experience is a blessing.

It makes you better.

Let me repeat that last sentence, because I know you glossed over it with a disbelieving smirk.

Pelvic organ prolapse will make you better. Stronger. Healthier.

Let these words guide you and be your inspiration:

I let go and I trust that all that happens is for the greater good. My path is before me, I cannot see the end, but I move forward with confidence and peace, knowing that life is not about fairness, it is about kindness and love. It is about holding on to this moment, and living in this moment as though it may be your last. Life is not about promises or warranties. I do not know what tomorrow holds or if it will even come. I can only live for the now, and in this moment be the absolute best me I can be. I will keep one eye on the path ahead of me but my focus will be here and now. I will let my trust and faith guide my feet down this path, knowing that if I always choose kindness and love I will live life with no regrets. I let go and I trust.

Lots of love, see you in eight years.

Me

Looking Forward, Glancing Behind

So if this was some feel good, inspirational story, I would end things by saying that I ran a marathon or climbed a mountain.

I have done neither of these. And no, I am not planning on doing anything so monumental and awe-inspiring.

First, this is not a story with an ending. My story is ongoing. Tomorrow everything could change and I might be preparing for surgery right away, or I might make it to my end goal - surgery after menopause. I don't know. I can't predict the future.

Second, my body does have limits. I believe with proper training I could probably do both those things. But you know what? I'm lazy. Not severely so, but the idea of training for a marathon or climbing a mountain is just too much for me. I run for fun and stress release but that is it.

Remember where I was when I got pregnant? I learned my lesson about burning out and I will not let myself take on too much. My boys are only little once. I don't want to miss any of these magical experiences that only come once in a child's life. I focus on the priorities - myself, Remy, Jace and Yonas. Everything else can get in line and I might get to it. That includes the laundry, dishes and mopping, they stay way at the bottom of the list.

In fact, being brutally honest, I don't run as much as I used to and that weight I lost, well, I put five pounds of it back on. That balance, it is always shifting. New priorities, such as writing, take time away from other things like workouts. It's always a balance.

Plus, chocolate is my stress relief and who knew elementary school was so stressful for the parents?

What I am doing is living my life, relatively pain free and without pelvic organ prolapse constantly on my mind. I am an active and involved mother. I have gone snowboarding with my kids. I am learning how to drive a race car (Oops, did I fail to mention that one? Spoilers! Maybe that adventure will be in my sequel). I go on family bike rides. I chase my boys and jump on the trampoline (a little, I'm not crazy!). More often than not I say 'yes, I can do that,' to my boys, instead of 'no, maybe later'. I am living life.

And it's good.

I know three years ago, living this life, this simple, happy, pain free life seemed like an impossible dream. But here I am, dreams can come true.

My greatest lesson through it all? Great things take time. On those dark days, when I craved seeing the proverbial light at the end of the tunnel, it seemed like I might never be whole again. But I remained dedicated to my treatments, more through desperation at times than anything else, and eventually learned the light was not at the end of some weird tunnel that I thought was wrapped around my life. The light was all around me. I just had to open up and let it in.

My body needed years to find a new, healthy, functional balance. Years. Seven years to be exact. Although only the last two years have been spent actively treating and caring for my POP with supplements, exercises, alignment and eStim. Perhaps my healing path would have been shorter if I had discovered these options sooner. I will never know.

Am I glad I took the path I did? Yes. I prefer

not to live with regrets. I made the best decisions I could at the time.

Can I maintain this new balance and lifestyle for the rest of my life? I doubt it. I suspect menopause may throw some serious curve balls my way, plus whatever life has in store for me. What I do proudly own are high hopes and a dedication to my treatments, and for now each day is one step closer to my goal. One more day living a full life, despite pelvic organ prolapse.

Will I have surgery? Yes, I expect I will. Even though the idea terrifies me. As I age, my symptoms are likely to worsen, even with all my treatments. At some point, when I feel I am ready, I will likely travel to have my surgery. For all the great things about our Canadian medical system, there are some weaknesses. The main one being a lack of specialists and insane waits to see the few good ones we have. Perhaps that will change once I am ready for surgery but, for now, I am not concerned. I will put my research cap back on when the time comes and find the best path for me when I reach that crossroads.

At the end of the day, my journey through life has been filled with a lot of ups and downs. Pregnancy should have been only a moment in my journey, a snap shot in time, instead it became a defining point where everything changed, that experience shaping every day from Jace's birth forward.

Pelvic organ prolapse no longer defines me. I can look on it now, with a little distance and knowledge, and see that it reshaped me, the shears of motherhood, in all their glory, hacking at me. Like a tree I am growing and expanding in new directions now, but I feel fuller and more beautiful for the cuts. Life changes and my greatest wish is that I can remain strong enough to face each change with grace and dignity. And preferably without peeing my pants.

Unless I am drinking wine and someone says something insanely funny. Then, all pant peeing bets are off.

And with that I will pause my story. Yes, only pause, because my story is far from over. There is still so much more life to come.

WHY?

Many people wonder why I talk about something so private... my privates... in such a very public way.

I am sure I offend many. I am sure some of my friends look at me in a different way, feeling perhaps they now know 'too much' about me.

So why would I expose myself this way? Why would I put it all out there in this book?

Because I am sick of the silence. I am sick of women suffering in silence. I am sick of women feeling embarrassed, ashamed, depressed.

I am sick of women living half-lives, not doing the things they love, because of pain, fear, discomfort and shame.

I am sick of women not knowing about POP until it happens to them.

I am sick of doctors not knowing about POP, or brushing it off as nothing to worry about.

I am sick of pelvic organ prolapse being a hidden epidemic that brings so many women nothing but pain, discomfort, shame, fear, depression, and sadness.

I want women to have hope.

I want women to be educated.

I want women to take pride and ownership of their bodies. We only get one, let's cherish and honor this amazing gift.

I want women around the world, suffering from POP, to know they are not alone.

I want women to know *before* POP happens that it can happen so they can take steps to try and protect themselves.

I want there to be progress. It is insanity that half of all females will develop POP, yet most doctors know almost nothing about the condition and the surgeries have insanely high failure and complication rates.

I want there to be hope. More research needs to be done into the causes of POP, then into safe and effective methods of treatment.

I want more funding to be put into researching effective and safe treatment options for women everywhere.

Why do I talk about my privates? Because I am angry and frustrated and fed up with the silence and suffering.

I do it because I have had so many women come to me and say, 'thank you'.

I know this book is not a literary masterpiece, but I hope it has served its purpose: simply to help at least one woman feel that she is not alone and give her some hope. Perhaps in hearing my story, she will see some of her own struggles and it will help her lift the veil and let in the light of hope.

To all my sisters around the world struggling

with pelvic organ prolapse, fistulas and other pelvic floor disorders, this book is dedicated to you.

You are the reason why.

Tips For Living With Prolapse

Go see your doctor. Listen to what they say, then go see another one, preferably one who specializes in the pelvic floor and urogynological issues. You may require multiple examinations before you gain a clear understanding of your specific issues. This is a field that many doctors have minimal training in, so seek out specialists whenever possible.

Research all your options. Every body is different, with different needs. What works for one woman, may not work for another. There are so many options for treatment, take the time to learn about all of them.

Consider visiting a physiotherapist who specializes in the pelvic floor. This is a rapidly growing field that offers a lot of benefits to women. They can teach you a lot about alignment, exercising and other techniques that could provide you with relief from symptoms and even improvement.

Experiment with your body. It takes time to adjust and heal when trying new treatments. Give yourself weeks or even months before you decide something is not working. If you do determine something is not helping, don't be discouraged. Try something else. Perhaps you need to add a supplement, exercise or complimentary therapy to make the treatment more effective. Or maybe the timing is simply wrong and at another place in your healing journey the therapy will provide benefits. Living with prolapse is about finding balance. Keep playing, it is possible to find a healthy, happy balance.

Don't underestimate the psychological impact of living with prolapse. There is no shame in seeking out help if you are struggling. A healthy, optimistic mind set can be extremely beneficial in living with POP.

Join some support groups. There is nothing better than joining forces with other women who understand. Today we have amazing opportunities through the internet to connect with women around the world.

Most people know surprisingly little about the health and safety of the pelvic floor. This is especially true in fitness circles. If it hurts, causes you to leak, or feels wrong, trust yourself and find something else. Once damage is done, it is very hard to correct. Always keep the prevention of damage, and protection of your pelvic floor, as your goal.

Believe in your body. If you take care of it, listen to it, support it, and give it the time it needs, you may be very surprised by what it can do. It may seem like your prolapse happened suddenly but, more than likely, it was developing over a great deal of time. Give it the tools and time it needs to strengthen and heal.

Invest in yourself. You only get one body, one mind. Take care of it. You're worth it.

COMING SOON FROM P.R. NEWTON

SHATTERED EMBRACE

Tory Witcraft wants nothing more than to be a mother. With her husband, Matt, they decide to adopt from Ethiopia, but her journey to motherhood is anything but smooth. Disapproving family members, mysterious delays, and the sudden bankruptcy of their adoption agency provide a rocky start to her life as a mother to a little girl named Bethlehem. But the worst has yet to come when Bethlehem's history of trauma, and resulting violent outbursts, revive Tory's own painful childhood memories. Can she overcome her own traumas to become the mother Bethlehem needs to heal, or will their lives be shattered by the one thing they both desire the most… family?

ABOUT THE AUTHOR

P.R. (Piper) Newton was born and raised in Canada. A one-time professional communications and public relations manager, she now spends her time raising her boys and writing stories that capture her heart, begging to be told.

To learn more visit her here:
www.prnewton.com

Made in the USA
Middletown, DE
20 October 2015